THE
MASH
Mindset Journal

This journal is dedicated to all of who you are!
The evolution, what is now and what has been.
I love you so much (your name here).
Thank you for trusting the journey.

With love and light,
Coach P

Hey you!

You know it's a big deal that you have this journal in your hands right? Yep a real big deal. This new journal represents a new chapter and maybe even a new book in your life. I'm so excited for your healing, unfolding, your expansion and your now. It's your time to unpack what was, appreciate what is now and write a new narrative that is direct alignment with the delicious life experiences you desire to have!

How to use the MASH Mindset Journal:

The MASH Mindset journal is a daily guided personal development journal filled with 90 day and night opportunities to begin your day with a daily Mindset Kickstart Session and unpack your day with the Relax and Release Night session. Follow the easy guided prompts and start your journey to your highest self.

Enjoy!
Coach P

Happy _____ *Today is My Day!*
(day of the week)

Today I feel:

Today I want to feel:

I am grateful for, excited about, appreciative of, looking forward to:

1. _____

2. _____

3. _____

Morning Mantra:

Today is my day. I am in abundance. I have everything I need inside of me to Make Amazing Shit Happen. Everything is always working out for me. I am whole and complete. I look forward to GOD moving the universe on my behalf. I said it is so and so it is.

I will take the actions below in order to reach my desired feeling for today. I will practice in my good and better serving feeling as often as I need to or desire to today. I am committed to reaching and maintaining my desired feeling today.

1. _____

2. _____

3. _____

My intention for today is:

_____
_____
_____
_____

How was your day? **Rate your day**

😃	😐	🙂	🙂	🙁	😟	😣
Amazing	Great	Good	OK	Bad	Terrible	It Sucked

I am grateful for, glad about, appreciative of, looking forward to:

1. _____

2. _____

3. _____

Reflection:

What did today teach you?

_____

_____

_____

What are you releasing from today?

_____

_____

_____

_____ I see you & I hear you.
Your Name

Take 3 deep long breaths in the nose & out of the mouth.

Center yourself in this thought/knowing that
"Everything is always working out for me."

Finish this sentence:

_____ I am so proud of you. Today you...
Your Name

_____

_____

Happy _____ *Today is My Day!*
(day of the week)

Today I feel:

Today I want to feel:

I am grateful for, excited about, appreciative of, looking forward to:

1. _____

2. _____

3. _____

Morning Mantra:

Today is my day. I am in abundance. I have everything I need inside of me to Make Amazing Shit Happen. Everything is always working out for me. I am whole and complete. I look forward to GOD moving the universe on my behalf. I said it is so and so it is.

I will take the actions below in order to reach my desired feeling for today. I will practice in my good and better serving feeling as often as I need to or desire to today. I am committed to reaching and maintaining my desired feeling today.

1. _____

2. _____

3. _____

My intention for today is:

_____
_____
_____
_____

How was your day? **Rate your day**

| Amazing | Great | Good | OK | Bad | Terrible | It Sucked |

I am grateful for, glad about, appreciative of, looking forward to:

1. _____

2. _____

3. _____

Reflection:

What did today teach you?

_____
_____
_____

What are you releasing from today?

_____
_____
_____

_____ I see you & I hear you.
Your Name

Take 3 deep long breaths in the nose & out of the mouth.

Center yourself in this thought/knowing that
"Everything is always working out for me."

Finish this sentence:

_____ I am so proud of you. Today you...
Your Name

_____
_____

Happy _____ *Today is My Day!*
(day of the week)

Today I feel:

Today I want to feel:

I am grateful for, excited about, appreciative of, looking forward to:

1. _____
2. _____
3. _____

Morning Mantra:

Today is my day. I am in abundance. I have everything I need inside of me to Make Amazing Shit Happen. Everything is always working out for me. I am whole and complete. I look forward to GOD moving the universe on my behalf. I said it is so and so it is.

I will take the actions below in order to reach my desired feeling for today. I will practice in my good and better serving feeling as often as I need to or desire to today. I am committed to reaching and maintaining my desired feeling today.

1. _____
2. _____
3. _____

My intention for today is:

_____
_____
_____
_____

How was your day? **Rate your day**

😬 Amazing 😐 Great 🙂 Good 🙂 OK 🙁 Bad 😞 Terrible 😣 It Sucked

I am grateful for, glad about, appreciative of, looking forward to:

1. _____

2. _____

3. _____

Reflection:

What did today teach you?

_____
_____
_____

What are you releasing from today?

_____
_____
_____

_____ I see you & I hear you.
Your Name

Take 3 deep long breaths in the nose & out of the mouth.

Center yourself in this thought/knowing that
"Everything is always working out for me."

Finish this sentence:

_____ I am so proud of you. Today you...
Your Name

_____
_____

Happy _____ _Today is My Day!_
(day of the week)

┌─── _Today I feel:_ ───┐   ┌─── _Today I want to feel:_ ───┐
│   │   │   │
│   │   │   │
│   │   │   │
│   │   │   │
└───────────────────────┘   └───────────────────────────────┘

I am grateful for, excited about, appreciative of, looking forward to:

1. _____

2. _____

3. _____

Morning Mantra:

Today is my day. I am in abundance. I have everything I need inside of me to Make Amazing Shit Happen. Everything is always working out for me. I am whole and complete. I look forward to GOD moving the universe on my behalf. I said it is so and so it is.

I will take the actions below in order to reach my desired feeling for today. I will practice in my good and better serving feeling as often as I need to or desire to today. I am committed to reaching and maintaining my desired feeling today.

1. _____

2. _____

3. _____

My intention for today is:

_____
_____
_____
_____

How was your day? **Rate your day**

Amazing	Great	Good	OK	Bad	Terrible	It Sucked

I am grateful for, glad about, appreciative of, looking forward to:

1. _____

2. _____

3. _____

Reflection:

What did today teach you?

_____

_____

_____

What are you releasing from today?

_____

_____

_____

_____ I see you & I hear you.
Your Name

Take 3 deep long breaths in the nose & out of the mouth.

Center yourself in this thought/knowing that
"Everything is always working out for me."

Finish this sentence:

_____ I am so proud of you. Today you...
Your Name

_____

_____

Happy _____
(day of the week)

Today is My Day!

┌─ *Today I feel:* ─┐

┌─ *Today I want to feel:* ─┐

I am grateful for, excited about, appreciative of, looking forward to:

1. _____

2. _____

3. _____

Morning Mantra:

Today is my day. I am in abundance. I have everything I need inside of me to Make Amazing Shit Happen. Everything is always working out for me. I am whole and complete. I look forward to GOD moving the universe on my behalf. I said it is so and so it is.

I will take the actions below in order to reach my desired feeling for today. I will practice in my good and better serving feeling as often as I need to or desire to today. I am committed to reaching and maintaining my desired feeling today.

1. _____

2. _____

3. _____

My intention for today is:

_____
_____
_____
_____

NIGHT TIME RELAX AND RELEASE SESSION

How was your day? **Rate your day**

| Amazing | Great | Good | OK | Bad | Terrible | It Sucked |

I am grateful for, glad about, appreciative of, looking forward to:

1. _____

2. _____

3. _____

Reflection:

What did today teach you?

_____

_____

_____

What are you releasing from today?

_____

_____

_____

_____

_____ I see you & I hear you.
Your Name

Take 3 deep long breaths in the nose & out of the mouth.

Center yourself in this thought/knowing that
"Everything is always working out for me."

Finish this sentence:

_____ I am so proud of you. Today you...
Your Name

_____

_____

Happy _____ *Today is My Day!*
(day of the week)

┌─ *Today I feel:* ─┐   ┌─ *Today I want to feel:* ─┐
│   │   │   │
│   │   │   │
│   │   │   │
│   │   │   │
│   │   │   │
└──────────────────┘   └──────────────────────────┘

I am grateful for, excited about, appreciative of, looking forward to:

1. _____

2. _____

3. _____

Morning Mantra:

Today is my day. I am in abundance. I have everything I need inside of me to Make Amazing Shit Happen. Everything is always working out for me. I am whole and complete. I look forward to GOD moving the universe on my behalf. I said it is so and so it is.

I will take the actions below in order to reach my desired feeling for today. I will practice in my good and better serving feeling as often as I need to or desire to today. I am committed to reaching and maintaining my desired feeling today.

1. _____

2. _____

3. _____

My intention for today is:

_____
_____
_____
_____

How was your day? **Rate your day**

Amazing	Great	Good	OK	Bad	Terrible	It Sucked

I am grateful for, glad about, appreciative of, looking forward to:

1. _____

2. _____

3. _____

Reflection:

What did today teach you?

_____
_____
_____

What are you releasing from today?

_____
_____
_____

_____ I see you & I hear you.
Your Name

Take 3 deep long breaths in the nose & out of the mouth.

Center yourself in this thought/knowing that
"Everything is always working out for me."

Finish this sentence:

_____ I am so proud of you. Today you...
Your Name

_____
_____

Happy _____   *Today is My Day!*
(day of the week)

┌─ *Today I feel:* ─┐   ┌─ *Today I want to feel:* ─┐

I am grateful for, excited about, appreciative of, looking forward to:

1. _____

2. _____

3. _____

Morning Mantra:

Today is my day. I am in abundance. I have everything I need inside of me to Make Amazing Shit Happen. Everything is always working out for me. I am whole and complete. I look forward to GOD moving the universe on my behalf. I said it is so and so it is.

I will take the actions below in order to reach my desired feeling for today. I will practice in my good and better serving feeling as often as I need to or desire to today. I am committed to reaching and maintaining my desired feeling today.

1. _____

2. _____

3. _____

My intention for today is:

_____
_____
_____
_____

NIGHT TIME RELAX AND RELEASE SESSION

How was your day? **Rate your day**

| :) Amazing | :\| Great | :) Good | :) OK | :(Bad | :(Terrible | >:< It Sucked |

I am grateful for, glad about, appreciative of, looking forward to:

1. _____

2. _____

3. _____

Reflection:

What did today teach you?

_____
_____
_____

What are you releasing from today?

_____
_____
_____

_____ I see you & I hear you.
Your Name

Take 3 deep long breaths in the nose & out of the mouth.

Center yourself in this thought/knowing that
"Everything is always working out for me."

Finish this sentence:

_____ I am so proud of you. Today you...
Your Name

_____
_____

Happy _____   *Today is My Day!*
(day of the week)

Today I feel:	*Today I want to feel:*

I am grateful for, excited about, appreciative of, looking forward to:

1. _____

2. _____

3. _____

Morning Mantra:

Today is my day. I am in abundance. I have everything I need inside of me to Make Amazing Shit Happen. Everything is always working out for me. I am whole and complete. I look forward to GOD moving the universe on my behalf. I said it is so and so it is.

I will take the actions below in order to reach my desired feeling for today. I will practice in my good and better serving feeling as often as I need to or desire to today. I am committed to reaching and maintaining my desired feeling today.

1. _____

2. _____

3. _____

My intention for today is:

_____
_____
_____
_____

How was your day? **Rate your day**

😋	😐	🙂	🙂	🙁	☹️	😣
Amazing	Great	Good	OK	Bad	Terrible	It Sucked

I am grateful for, glad about, appreciative of, looking forward to:

1. _____

2. _____

3. _____

Reflection:

What did today teach you?

_____
_____
_____

What are you releasing from today?

_____
_____
_____

_____ I see you & I hear you.
Your Name

Take 3 deep long breaths in the nose & out of the mouth.

Center yourself in this thought/knowing that
"Everything is always working out for me."

Finish this sentence:

_____ I am so proud of you. Today you...
Your Name

_____
_____

Happy _____ Today is My Day!
(day of the week)

┌─ Today I feel: ─┐   ┌─ Today I want to feel: ─┐
│   │   │   │
│   │   │   │
│   │   │   │
└─────────────────┘   └─────────────────────────┘

I am grateful for, excited about, appreciative of, looking forward to:

1. _____

2. _____

3. _____

Morning Mantra:

Today is my day. I am in abundance. I have everything I need inside of me to Make Amazing Shit Happen. Everything is always working out for me. I am whole and complete. I look forward to GOD moving the universe on my behalf. I said it is so and so it is.

I will take the actions below in order to reach my desired feeling for today. I will practice in my good and better serving feeling as often as I need to or desire to today. I am committed to reaching and maintaining my desired feeling today.

1. _____

2. _____

3. _____

My intention for today is:

_____
_____
_____
_____

How was your day? **Rate your day**

Amazing	Great	Good	OK	Bad	Terrible	It Sucked

I am grateful for, glad about, appreciative of, looking forward to:

1. _____

2. _____

3. _____

Reflection:

What did today teach you?

_____
_____
_____

What are you releasing from today?

_____
_____
_____

_____ I see you & I hear you.
Your Name

Take 3 deep long breaths in the nose & out of the mouth.

Center yourself in this thought/knowing that
"Everything is always working out for me."

Finish this sentence:

_____ I am so proud of you. Today you...
Your Name

_____
_____

Happy _____   _Today is My Day!_
(day of the week)

┌─ _Today I feel:_ ─┐   ┌─ _Today I want to feel:_ ─┐

I am grateful for, excited about, appreciative of, looking forward to:

1. _____

2. _____

3. _____

Morning Mantra:

Today is my day. I am in abundance. I have everything I need inside of me to Make Amazing Shit Happen. Everything is always working out for me. I am whole and complete. I look forward to GOD moving the universe on my behalf. I said it is so and so it is.

I will take the actions below in order to reach my desired feeling for today. I will practice in my good and better serving feeling as often as I need to or desire to today. I am committed to reaching and maintaining my desired feeling today.

1. _____

2. _____

3. _____

My intention for today is:

_____
_____
_____
_____

How was your day? **Rate your day**

:-D	:-|	:-)	:-)	:-(	:-(	>-<
Amazing	Great	Good	OK	Bad	Terrible	It Sucked

I am grateful for, glad about, appreciative of, looking forward to:

1. _____

2. _____

3. _____

Reflection:

What did today teach you?

_____
_____
_____

What are you releasing from today?

_____
_____
_____

_____ I see you & I hear you.
Your Name

Take 3 deep long breaths in the nose & out of the mouth.

Center yourself in this thought/knowing that
"Everything is always working out for me."

Finish this sentence:

_____ I am so proud of you. Today you...
Your Name

_____
_____

Happy _____ *Today is My Day!*
(day of the week)

┌─── *Today I feel:* ───┐   ┌─── *Today I want to feel:* ───┐

I am grateful for, excited about, appreciative of, looking forward to:

1. _____
2. _____
3. _____

Morning Mantra:

Today is my day. I am in abundance. I have everything I need inside of me to Make Amazing Shit Happen. Everything is always working out for me. I am whole and complete. I look forward to GOD moving the universe on my behalf. I said it is so and so it is.

I will take the actions below in order to reach my desired feeling for today. I will practice in my good and better serving feeling as often as I need to or desire to today. I am committed to reaching and maintaining my desired feeling today.

1. _____
2. _____
3. _____

My intention for today is:

_____
_____
_____
_____

NIGHT TIME RELAX AND RELEASE SESSION

How was your day? **Rate your day**

| Amazing | Great | Good | OK | Bad | Terrible | It Sucked |

I am grateful for, glad about, appreciative of, looking forward to:

1. _____

2. _____

3. _____

Reflection:

What did today teach you?

_____
_____
_____

What are you releasing from today?

_____
_____
_____

_____ I see you & I hear you.
Your Name

Take 3 deep long breaths in the nose & out of the mouth.

Center yourself in this thought/knowing that
"Everything is always working out for me."

Finish this sentence:

_____ I am so proud of you. Today you...
Your Name

_____
_____

Happy _____ *Today is My Day!*
(day of the week)

┌─ *Today I feel:* ─┐   ┌─ *Today I want to feel:* ─┐

I am grateful for, excited about, appreciative of, looking forward to:

1. _____

2. _____

3. _____

Morning Mantra:

Today is my day. I am in abundance. I have everything I need inside of me to Make Amazing Shit Happen. Everything is always working out for me. I am whole and complete. I look forward to GOD moving the universe on my behalf. I said it is so and so it is.

I will take the actions below in order to reach my desired feeling for today. I will practice in my good and better serving feeling as often as I need to or desire to today. I am committed to reaching and maintaining my desired feeling today.

1. _____

2. _____

3. _____

My intention for today is:

_____
_____
_____
_____
_____

How was your day ? **Rate your day**

| Amazing | Great | Good | OK | Bad | Terrible | It Sucked |

I am grateful for, glad about, appreciative of, looking forward to:

1. _____

2. _____

3. _____

Reflection:

What did today teach you?

_____

_____

_____

What are you releasing from today?

_____

_____

_____

_____ I see you & I hear you.
Your Name

Take 3 deep long breaths in the nose & out of the mouth.

Center yourself in this thought/knowing that
"Everything is always working out for me."

Finish this sentence:

_____ I am so proud of you. Today you...
Your Name

_____

_____

MORNING MINDSET SESSION

Happy _____   *Today is My Day!*
(day of the week)

Today I feel:	*Today I want to feel:*

I am grateful for, excited about, appreciative of, looking forward to:

1. _____

2. _____

3. _____

Morning Mantra:

Today is my day. I am in abundance. I have everything I need inside of me to Make Amazing Shit Happen. Everything is always working out for me. I am whole and complete. I look forward to GOD moving the universe on my behalf. I said it is so and so it is.

I will take the actions below in order to reach my desired feeling for today. I will practice in my good and better serving feeling as often as I need to or desire to today. I am committed to reaching and maintaining my desired feeling today.

1. _____

2. _____

3. _____

My intention for today is:

_____
_____
_____
_____

NIGHT TIME RELAX AND RELEASE SESSION

How was your day? **Rate your day**

😀 Amazing   😐 Great   🙂 Good   🙂 OK   🙁 Bad   😟 Terrible   😣 It Sucked

I am grateful for, glad about, appreciative of, looking forward to:

1. _____

2. _____

3. _____

Reflection:

What did today teach you?

_____
_____
_____

What are you releasing from today?

_____
_____
_____

_____ I see you & I hear you.
Your Name

Take 3 deep long breaths in the nose & out of the mouth.

Center yourself in this thought/knowing that
"Everything is always working out for me."

Finish this sentence:

_____ I am so proud of you. Today you...
Your Name

_____
_____

Happy _____   *Today is My Day!*
(day of the week)

Today I feel: *Today I want to feel:*

I am grateful for, excited about, appreciative of, looking forward to:

1. _____

2. _____

3. _____

Morning Mantra:

Today is my day. I am in abundance. I have everything I need inside of me to Make Amazing Shit Happen. Everything is always working out for me. I am whole and complete. I look forward to GOD moving the universe on my behalf. I said it is so and so it is.

I will take the actions below in order to reach my desired feeling for today. I will practice in my good and better serving feeling as often as I need to or desire to today. I am committed to reaching and maintaining my desired feeling today.

1. _____

2. _____

3. _____

My intention for today is:

_____
_____
_____
_____

How was your day? **Rate your day**

Amazing   Great   Good   OK   Bad   Terrible   It Sucked

I am grateful for, glad about, appreciative of, looking forward to:

1. _____

2. _____

3. _____

Reflection:

What did today teach you?

_____
_____
_____

What are you releasing from today?

_____
_____
_____

_____ I see you & I hear you.
Your Name

Take 3 deep long breaths in the nose & out of the mouth.

Center yourself in this thought/knowing that
"Everything is always working out for me."

Finish this sentence:

_____ I am so proud of you. Today you...
Your Name

_____
_____

Happy _____
(day of the week)

Today is My Day!

┌──── Today I feel: ────┐   ┌──── Today I want to feel: ────┐

I am grateful for, excited about, appreciative of, looking forward to:

1. _____

2. _____

3. _____

Morning Mantra:

Today is my day. I am in abundance. I have everything I need inside of me to Make Amazing Shit Happen. Everything is always working out for me. I am whole and complete. I look forward to GOD moving the universe on my behalf. I said it is so and so it is.

I will take the actions below in order to reach my desired feeling for today. I will practice in my good and better serving feeling as often as I need to or desire to today. I am committed to reaching and maintaining my desired feeling today.

1. _____

2. _____

3. _____

My intention for today is:

_____
_____
_____
_____
_____

NIGHT TIME RELAX AND RELEASE SESSION

How was your day? **Rate your day**

😁	😛	🙂	😊	🙁	😣	😖
Amazing	Great	Good	OK	Bad	Terrible	It Sucked

I am grateful for, glad about, appreciative of, looking forward to:

1. _____

2. _____

3. _____

Reflection:

What did today teach you?

_____
_____
_____

What are you releasing from today?

_____
_____
_____

_____ I see you & I hear you.
Your Name

Take 3 deep long breaths in the nose & out of the mouth.

Center yourself in this thought/knowing that
"Everything is always working out for me."

Finish this sentence:

_____ I am so proud of you. Today you...
Your Name

_____
_____

Happy _____   *Today is My Day!*
(day of the week)

┌─── *Today I feel:* ───┐   ┌─── *Today I want to feel:* ───┐

I am grateful for, excited about, appreciative of, looking forward to:

1. _____

2. _____

3. _____

Morning Mantra:

Today is my day. I am in abundance. I have everything I need inside of me to Make Amazing Shit Happen. Everything is always working out for me. I am whole and complete. I look forward to GOD moving the universe on my behalf. I said it is so and so it is.

I will take the actions below in order to reach my desired feeling for today. I will practice in my good and better serving feeling as often as I need to or desire to today. I am committed to reaching and maintaining my desired feeling today.

1. _____

2. _____

3. _____

My intention for today is:

_____
_____
_____
_____

How was your day? **Rate your day**

Amazing	Great	Good	OK	Bad	Terrible	It Sucked

I am grateful for, glad about, appreciative of, looking forward to:

1. _____

2. _____

3. _____

Reflection:

What did today teach you?

_____
_____
_____

What are you releasing from today?

_____
_____
_____

_____ I see you & I hear you.
Your Name

Take 3 deep long breaths in the nose & out of the mouth.

Center yourself in this thought/knowing that
"Everything is always working out for me."

Finish this sentence:

_____ I am so proud of you. Today you...
Your Name

_____
_____

Happy _____ Today is My Day!
(day of the week)

┌─── Today I feel: ───┐   ┌─── Today I want to feel: ───┐
│   │   │   │
│   │   │   │
│   │   │   │
│   │   │   │
└─────────────────────┘   └─────────────────────────────┘

I am grateful for, excited about, appreciative of, looking forward to:

1. _____

2. _____

3. _____

Morning Mantra:

Today is my day. I am in abundance. I have everything I need inside of me to Make Amazing Shit Happen. Everything is always working out for me. I am whole and complete. I look forward to GOD moving the universe on my behalf. I said it is so and so it is.

I will take the actions below in order to reach my desired feeling for today. I will practice in my good and better serving feeling as often as I need to or desire to today. I am committed to reaching and maintaining my desired feeling today.

1. _____

2. _____

3. _____

My intention for today is:

_____
_____
_____
_____

NIGHT TIME RELAX AND RELEASE SESSION

How was your day ? **Rate your day**

😀	😐	🙂	🙂	🙁	😣	😖
Amazing	Great	Good	OK	Bad	Terrible	It Sucked

I am grateful for, glad about, appreciative of, looking forward to:

1. _____

2. _____

3. _____

Reflection:

What did today teach you?

_____
_____
_____

What are you releasing from today?

_____
_____
_____
_____

_____ I see you & I hear you.
Your Name

Take 3 deep long breaths in the nose & out of the mouth.

Center yourself in this thought/knowing that
"Everything is always working out for me."

Finish this sentence:

_____ I am so proud of you. Today you...
Your Name

_____
_____

Happy _____   *Today is My Day!*
(day of the week)

┌─ *Today I feel:* ─┐   ┌─ *Today I want to feel:* ─┐

I am grateful for, excited about, appreciative of, looking forward to:

1. _____

2. _____

3. _____

Morning Mantra:

Today is my day. I am in abundance. I have everything I need inside of me to Make Amazing Shit Happen. Everything is always working out for me. I am whole and complete. I look forward to GOD moving the universe on my behalf. I said it is so and so it is.

I will take the actions below in order to reach my desired feeling for today. I will practice in my good and better serving feeling as often as I need to or desire to today. I am committed to reaching and maintaining my desired feeling today.

1. _____

2. _____

3. _____

My intention for today is:

_____
_____
_____
_____

How was your day? **Rate your day**

😄   😐   🙂   🙂   🙁   ☹️   😣

Amazing   Great   Good   OK   Bad   Terrible   It Sucked

I am grateful for, glad about, appreciative of, looking forward to:

1. _____

2. _____

3. _____

Reflection:

What did today teach you?

_____

_____

_____

What are you releasing from today?

_____

_____

_____

_____ I see you & I hear you.
Your Name

Take 3 deep long breaths in the nose & out of the mouth.

Center yourself in this thought/knowing that
"Everything is always working out for me."

Finish this sentence:

_____ I am so proud of you. Today you...
Your Name

_____

_____

MORNING MINDSET SESSION

Happy _____ *Today is My Day!*
(day of the week)

Today I feel:

Today I want to feel:

I am grateful for, excited about, appreciative of, looking forward to:

1. _____

2. _____

3. _____

Morning Mantra:

Today is my day. I am in abundance. I have everything I need inside of me to Make Amazing Shit Happen. Everything is always working out for me. I am whole and complete. I look forward to GOD moving the universe on my behalf. I said it is so and so it is.

I will take the actions below in order to reach my desired feeling for today. I will practice in my good and better serving feeling as often as I need to or desire to today. I am committed to reaching and maintaining my desired feeling today.

1. _____

2. _____

3. _____

My intention for today is:

_____
_____
_____
_____

NIGHT TIME RELAX AND RELEASE SESSION

How was your day? **Rate your day**

:-)	:-|	:-)	:-)	:-(	:-(	>:<
Amazing	Great	Good	OK	Bad	Terrible	It Sucked

I am grateful for, glad about, appreciative of, looking forward to:

1. _____

2. _____

3. _____

Reflection:

What did today teach you?

_____

_____

_____

What are you releasing from today?

_____

_____

_____

_____ I see you & I hear you.
Your Name

Take 3 deep long breaths in the nose & out of the mouth.

Center yourself in this thought/knowing that
"Everything is always working out for me."

Finish this sentence:

_____ I am so proud of you. Today you...
Your Name

_____

_____

Happy _____ *Today is My Day!*
(day of the week)

Today I feel:

Today I want to feel:

I am grateful for, excited about, appreciative of, looking forward to:

1. _____

2. _____

3. _____

Morning Mantra:

Today is my day. I am in abundance. I have everything I need inside of me to Make Amazing Shit Happen. Everything is always working out for me. I am whole and complete. I look forward to GOD moving the universe on my behalf. I said it is so and so it is.

I will take the actions below in order to reach my desired feeling for today. I will practice in my good and better serving feeling as often as I need to or desire to today. I am committed to reaching and maintaining my desired feeling today.

1. _____

2. _____

3. _____

My intention for today is:

_____
_____
_____
_____

How was your day? **Rate your day**

Amazing	Great	Good	OK	Bad	Terrible	It Sucked

I am grateful for, glad about, appreciative of, looking forward to:

1. _____

2. _____

3. _____

Reflection:

What did today teach you?

_____
_____
_____

What are you releasing from today?

_____
_____
_____

_____ I see you & I hear you.
Your Name

Take 3 deep long breaths in the nose & out of the mouth.

Center yourself in this thought/knowing that
"Everything is always working out for me."

Finish this sentence:

_____ I am so proud of you. Today you...
Your Name

_____
_____

Happy _____ Today is My Day!
(day of the week)

┌─ Today I feel: ─┐   ┌─ Today I want to feel: ─┐

I am grateful for, excited about, appreciative of, looking forward to:

1. _____

2. _____

3. _____

Morning Mantra:

Today is my day. I am in abundance. I have everything I need inside of me to Make Amazing Shit Happen. Everything is always working out for me. I am whole and complete. I look forward to GOD moving the universe on my behalf. I said it is so and so it is.

I will take the actions below in order to reach my desired feeling for today. I will practice in my good and better serving feeling as often as I need to or desire to today. I am committed to reaching and maintaining my desired feeling today.

1. _____

2. _____

3. _____

My intention for today is:

_____
_____
_____
_____

How was your day? **Rate your day**

😁 😬 😊 🙂 🙁 😧 😣
Amazing Great Good OK Bad Terrible It Sucked

I am grateful for, glad about, appreciative of, looking forward to:

1. _____

2. _____

3. _____

Reflection:

What did today teach you?

_____
_____
_____

What are you releasing from today?

_____
_____
_____

_____ I see you & I hear you.
Your Name

Take 3 deep long breaths in the nose & out of the mouth.

Center yourself in this thought/knowing that
"Everything is always working out for me."

Finish this sentence:

_____ I am so proud of you. Today you...
Your Name

_____
_____

Happy _____
(day of the week)

Today is My Day!

Today I feel:

Today I want to feel:

I am grateful for, excited about, appreciative of, looking forward to:

1. _____

2. _____

3. _____

Morning Mantra:

Today is my day. I am in abundance. I have everything I need inside of me to Make Amazing Shit Happen. Everything is always working out for me. I am whole and complete. I look forward to GOD moving the universe on my behalf. I said it is so and so it is.

I will take the actions below in order to reach my desired feeling for today. I will practice in my good and better serving feeling as often as I need to or desire to today. I am committed to reaching and maintaining my desired feeling today.

1. _____

2. _____

3. _____

My intention for today is:

_____
_____
_____
_____

How was your day? **Rate your day**

Amazing	Great	Good	OK	Bad	Terrible	It Sucked

I am grateful for, glad about, appreciative of, looking forward to:

1. _____

2. _____

3. _____

Reflection:

What did today teach you?

_____
_____
_____

What are you releasing from today?

_____
_____
_____

_____ I see you & I hear you.
Your Name

Take 3 deep long breaths in the nose & out of the mouth.

Center yourself in this thought/knowing that
"Everything is always working out for me."

Finish this sentence:

_____ I am so proud of you. Today you...
Your Name

_____
_____

Happy _____ *Today is My Day!*
(day of the week)

Today I feel: *Today I want to feel:*

I am grateful for, excited about, appreciative of, looking forward to:

1. _____

2. _____

3. _____

Morning Mantra:

Today is my day. I am in abundance. I have everything I need inside of me to Make Amazing Shit Happen. Everything is always working out for me. I am whole and complete. I look forward to GOD moving the universe on my behalf. I said it is so and so it is.

I will take the actions below in order to reach my desired feeling for today. I will practice in my good and better serving feeling as often as I need to or desire to today. I am committed to reaching and maintaining my desired feeling today.

1. _____

2. _____

3. _____

My intention for today is:

_____
_____
_____
_____

NIGHT TIME RELAX AND RELEASE SESSION

How was your day? **Rate your day**

| Amazing | Great | Good | OK | Bad | Terrible | It Sucked |

I am grateful for, glad about, appreciative of, looking forward to:

1. _____

2. _____

3. _____

Reflection:

What did today teach you?

_____
_____
_____

What are you releasing from today?

_____
_____
_____

_____ I see you & I hear you.
Your Name

Take 3 deep long breaths in the nose & out of the mouth.

Center yourself in this thought/knowing that
"Everything is always working out for me."

Finish this sentence:

_____ I am so proud of you. Today you...
Your Name

_____
_____

Happy _____ **(day of the week)**   *Today is My Day!*

┌─── *Today I feel:* ───┐   ┌─── *Today I want to feel:* ───┐

I am grateful for, excited about, appreciative of, looking forward to:

1. _____

2. _____

3. _____

Morning Mantra:

Today is my day. I am in abundance. I have everything I need inside of me to Make Amazing Shit Happen. Everything is always working out for me. I am whole and complete. I look forward to GOD moving the universe on my behalf. I said it is so and so it is.

I will take the actions below in order to reach my desired feeling for today. I will practice in my good and better serving feeling as often as I need to or desire to today. I am committed to reaching and maintaining my desired feeling today.

1. _____

2. _____

3. _____

My intention for today is:

_____

_____

_____

_____

How was your day? **Rate your day**

😀	😐	🙂	🙂	🙁	☹️	😣
Amazing	Great	Good	OK	Bad	Terrible	It Sucked

I am grateful for, glad about, appreciative of, looking forward to:

1. _____

2. _____

3. _____

Reflection:

What did today teach you?

_____
_____

_____

What are you releasing from today?

_____
_____
_____

_____ I see you & I hear you.
Your Name

Take 3 deep long breaths in the nose & out of the mouth.

Center yourself in this thought/knowing that
"Everything is always working out for me."

Finish this sentence:

_____ I am so proud of you. Today you...
Your Name

_____
_____

Happy _____ *Today is My Day!*
(day of the week)

┌─ *Today I feel:* ─┐ ┌─ *Today I want to feel:* ─┐

I am grateful for, excited about, appreciative of, looking forward to:

1. _____

2. _____

3. _____

Morning Mantra:

Today is my day. I am in abundance. I have everything I need inside of me to Make Amazing Shit Happen. Everything is always working out for me. I am whole and complete. I look forward to GOD moving the universe on my behalf. I said it is so and so it is.

I will take the actions below in order to reach my desired feeling for today. I will practice in my good and better serving feeling as often as I need to or desire to today. I am committed to reaching and maintaining my desired feeling today.

1. _____

2. _____

3. _____

My intention for today is:

_____
_____
_____
_____

NIGHT TIME RELAX AND RELEASE SESSION

How was your day? **Rate your day**

Amazing	Great	Good	OK	Bad	Terrible	It Sucked

I am grateful for, glad about, appreciative of, looking forward to:

1. _____

2. _____

3. _____

Reflection:

What did today teach you?

_____

_____

_____

What are you releasing from today?

_____

_____

_____

_____ I see you & I hear you.
Your Name

Take 3 deep long breaths in the nose & out of the mouth.

Center yourself in this thought/knowing that
"Everything is always working out for me."

Finish this sentence:

_____ I am so proud of you. Today you...
Your Name

_____

_____

Happy _____ Today is My Day!
(day of the week)

┌─── Today I feel: ───┐   ┌─── Today I want to feel: ───┐

I am grateful for, excited about, appreciative of, looking forward to:

1. _____

2. _____

3. _____

Morning Mantra:

Today is my day. I am in abundance. I have everything I need inside of me to Make Amazing Shit Happen. Everything is always working out for me. I am whole and complete. I look forward to GOD moving the universe on my behalf. I said it is so and so it is.

I will take the actions below in order to reach my desired feeling for today. I will practice in my good and better serving feeling as often as I need to or desire to to-day. I am committed to reaching and maintaining my desired feeling today.

1. _____

2. _____

3. _____

My intention for today is:

_____
_____
_____
_____
_____

How was your day ? **Rate your day**

Amazing	Great	Good	OK	Bad	Terrible	It Sucked

I am grateful for, glad about, appreciative of, looking forward to:

1. _____

2. _____

3. _____

Reflection:

What did today teach you?

_____
_____
_____

What are you releasing from today?

_____
_____
_____

_____ I see you & I hear you.
Your Name

Take 3 deep long breaths in the nose & out of the mouth.

Center yourself in this thought/knowing that
"Everything is always working out for me."

Finish this sentence:

_____ I am so proud of you. Today you...
Your Name

_____
_____

Happy _____ Today is My Day!
(day of the week)

┌─ Today I feel: ─┐   ┌─ Today I want to feel: ─┐

I am grateful for, excited about, appreciative of, looking forward to:

1. _____

2. _____

3. _____

Morning Mantra:

Today is my day. I am in abundance. I have everything I need inside of me to Make Amazing Shit Happen. Everything is always working out for me. I am whole and complete. I look forward to GOD moving the universe on my behalf. I said it is so and so it is.

I will take the actions below in order to reach my desired feeling for today. I will practice in my good and better serving feeling as often as I need to or desire to today. I am committed to reaching and maintaining my desired feeling today.

1. _____

2. _____

3. _____

My intention for today is:

_____
_____
_____
_____

NIGHT TIME RELAX AND RELEASE SESSION

How was your day? **Rate your day**

Amazing	Great	Good	OK	Bad	Terrible	It Sucked

I am grateful for, glad about, appreciative of, looking forward to:

1. _____

2. _____

3. _____

Reflection:

What did today teach you?

_____
_____
_____

What are you releasing from today?

_____
_____
_____

_____ I see you & I hear you.
Your Name

Take 3 deep long breaths in the nose & out of the mouth.

Center yourself in this thought/knowing that
"Everything is always working out for me."

Finish this sentence:

_____ I am so proud of you. Today you...
Your Name

_____
_____

Happy _____ *Today is My Day!*
(day of the week)

┌─ *Today I feel:* ─┐   ┌─ *Today I want to feel:* ─┐

I am grateful for, excited about, appreciative of, looking forward to:

1. _____

2. _____

3. _____

Morning Mantra:

Today is my day. I am in abundance. I have everything I need inside of me to Make Amazing Shit Happen. Everything is always working out for me. I am whole and complete. I look forward to GOD moving the universe on my behalf. I said it is so and so it is.

I will take the actions below in order to reach my desired feeling for today. I will practice in my good and better serving feeling as often as I need to or desire to today. I am committed to reaching and maintaining my desired feeling today.

1. _____

2. _____

3. _____

My intention for today is:

_____
_____
_____
_____

How was your day? Rate your day

Amazing	Great	Good	OK	Bad	Terrible	It Sucked

I am grateful for, glad about, appreciative of, looking forward to:

1. _____

2. _____

3. _____

Reflection:

What did today teach you?

_____
_____
_____

What are you releasing from today?

_____
_____
_____

_____ I see you & I hear you.
Your Name

Take 3 deep long breaths in the nose & out of the mouth.

Center yourself in this thought/knowing that
"Everything is always working out for me."

Finish this sentence:

_____ I am so proud of you. Today you...
Your Name

_____
_____

Happy _____   *Today is My Day!*

(day of the week)

┌─ *Today I feel:* ─┐   ┌─ *Today I want to feel:* ─┐

I am grateful for, excited about, appreciative of, looking forward to:

1. _____

2. _____

3. _____

Morning Mantra:

Today is my day. I am in abundance. I have everything I need inside of me to Make Amazing Shit Happen. Everything is always working out for me. I am whole and complete. I look forward to GOD moving the universe on my behalf. I said it is so and so it is.

I will take the actions below in order to reach my desired feeling for today. I will practice in my good and better serving feeling as often as I need to or desire to today. I am committed to reaching and maintaining my desired feeling today.

1. _____

2. _____

3. _____

My intention for today is:

_____
_____
_____
_____

NIGHT TIME RELAX AND RELEASE SESSION

How was your day? **Rate your day**

| Amazing | Great | Good | OK | Bad | Terrible | It Sucked |

I am grateful for, glad about, appreciative of, looking forward to:

1. _____

2. _____

3. _____

Reflection:

What did today teach you?

_____

_____

_____

What are you releasing from today?

_____

_____

_____

_____

_____ I see you & I hear you.
Your Name

Take 3 deep long breaths in the nose & out of the mouth.

Center yourself in this thought/knowing that
"Everything is always working out for me."

Finish this sentence:

_____ I am so proud of you. Today you...
Your Name

_____

_____

Happy _____   *Today is My Day!*
(day of the week)

┌─ *Today I feel:* ─┐   ┌─ *Today I want to feel:* ─┐

I am grateful for, excited about, appreciative of, looking forward to:

1. _____

2. _____

3. _____

Morning Mantra:

Today is my day. I am in abundance. I have everything I need inside of me to Make Amazing Shit Happen. Everything is always working out for me. I am whole and complete. I look forward to GOD moving the universe on my behalf. I said it is so and so it is.

I will take the actions below in order to reach my desired feeling for today. I will practice in my good and better serving feeling as often as I need to or desire to today. I am committed to reaching and maintaining my desired feeling today.

1. _____

2. _____

3. _____

My intention for today is:

_____
_____
_____
_____

How was your day? **Rate your day**

😃	😐	🙂	🙂	🙁	☹️	😣
Amazing	Great	Good	OK	Bad	Terrible	It Sucked

I am grateful for, glad about, appreciative of, looking forward to:

1. _____

2. _____

3. _____

Reflection:

What did today teach you?

_____
_____
_____

What are you releasing from today?

_____
_____
_____

_____ I see you & I hear you.
Your Name

Take 3 deep long breaths in the nose & out of the mouth.

Center yourself in this thought/knowing that
"Everything is always working out for me."

Finish this sentence:

_____ I am so proud of you. Today you...
Your Name

_____
_____

Happy _____   *Today is My Day!*
(day of the week)

┌─── *Today I feel:* ───┐   ┌─── *Today I want to feel:* ───┐

I am grateful for, excited about, appreciative of, looking forward to:

1. _____

2. _____

3. _____

Morning Mantra:

Today is my day. I am in abundance. I have everything I need inside of me to Make Amazing Shit Happen. Everything is always working out for me. I am whole and complete. I look forward to GOD moving the universe on my behalf. I said it is so and so it is.

I will take the actions below in order to reach my desired feeling for today. I will practice in my good and better serving feeling as often as I need to or desire to today. I am committed to reaching and maintaining my desired feeling today.

1. _____

2. _____

3. _____

My intention for today is:

_____
_____
_____
_____

NIGHT TIME RELAX AND RELEASE SESSION

How was your day? **Rate your day**

| Amazing | Great | Good | OK | Bad | Terrible | It Sucked |

I am grateful for, glad about, appreciative of, looking forward to:

1. _____

2. _____

3. _____

Reflection:

What did today teach you?

_____
_____
_____

What are you releasing from today?

_____
_____
_____

_____ I see you & I hear you.
Your Name

Take 3 deep long breaths in the nose & out of the mouth.

Center yourself in this thought/knowing that
"Everything is always working out for me."

Finish this sentence:

_____ I am so proud of you. Today you...
Your Name

_____
_____

Happy _____ *Today is My Day!*
(day of the week)

┌─ *Today I feel:* ─┐ ┌─ *Today I want to feel:* ─┐

I am grateful for, excited about, appreciative of, looking forward to:

1. _____

2. _____

3. _____

Morning Mantra:

Today is my day. I am in abundance. I have everything I need inside of me to Make Amazing Shit Happen. Everything is always working out for me. I am whole and complete. I look forward to GOD moving the universe on my behalf. I said it is so and so it is.

I will take the actions below in order to reach my desired feeling for today. I will practice in my good and better serving feeling as often as I need to or desire to today. I am committed to reaching and maintaining my desired feeling today.

1. _____

2. _____

3. _____

My intention for today is:

_____
_____
_____
_____

How was your day ? **Rate your day**

| Amazing | Great | Good | OK | Bad | Terrible | It Sucked |

I am grateful for, glad about, appreciative of, looking forward to:

1. _____

2. _____

3. _____

Reflection:

What did today teach you?

_____
_____
_____

What are you releasing from today?

_____
_____
_____

_____ I see you & I hear you.
Your Name

Take 3 deep long breaths in the nose & out of the mouth.

Center yourself in this thought/knowing that
"Everything is always working out for me."

Finish this sentence:

_____ I am so proud of you. Today you...
Your Name

_____
_____

Happy _____
(day of the week)

Today is My Day!

┌─── Today I feel: ───┐ ┌─── Today I want to feel: ───┐

I am grateful for, excited about, appreciative of, looking forward to:

1. _____

2. _____

3. _____

Morning Mantra:

Today is my day. I am in abundance. I have everything I need inside of me to Make Amazing Shit Happen. Everything is always working out for me. I am whole and complete. I look forward to GOD moving the universe on my behalf. I said it is so and so it is.

I will take the actions below in order to reach my desired feeling for today. I will practice in my good and better serving feeling as often as I need to or desire to today. I am committed to reaching and maintaining my desired feeling today.

1. _____

2. _____

3. _____

My intention for today is:

_____
_____
_____
_____

NIGHT TIME RELAX AND RELEASE SESSION

How was your day? Rate your day

Amazing	Great	Good	OK	Bad	Terrible	It Sucked

I am grateful for, glad about, appreciative of, looking forward to:

1. _____

2. _____

3. _____

Reflection:

What did today teach you?

_____

_____

_____

What are you releasing from today?

_____

_____

_____

_____ I see you & I hear you.
Your Name

Take 3 deep long breaths in the nose & out of the mouth.

Center yourself in this thought/knowing that
"Everything is always working out for me."

Finish this sentence:

_____ I am so proud of you. Today you...
Your Name

_____

_____

Happy _____   *Today is My Day!*
(day of the week)

┌─ *Today I feel:* ─┐   ┌─ *Today I want to feel:* ─┐
│   │   │   │
│   │   │   │
│   │   │   │
│   │   │   │
└───────────────────┘   └────────────────────────────┘

I am grateful for, excited about, appreciative of, looking forward to:

1. _____

2. _____

3. _____

Morning Mantra:

Today is my day. I am in abundance. I have everything I need inside of me to Make Amazing Shit Happen. Everything is always working out for me. I am whole and complete. I look forward to GOD moving the universe on my behalf. I said it is so and so it is.

I will take the actions below in order to reach my desired feeling for today. I will practice in my good and better serving feeling as often as I need to or desire to to-day. I am committed to reaching and maintaining my desired feeling today.

1. _____

2. _____

3. _____

My intention for today is:

_____
_____
_____
_____

How was your day? **Rate your day**

Amazing	Great	Good	OK	Bad	Terrible	It Sucked

I am grateful for, glad about, appreciative of, looking forward to:

1. _____

2. _____

3. _____

Reflection:

What did today teach you?

_____

_____

_____

What are you releasing from today?

_____

_____

_____

_____ I see you & I hear you.
Your Name

Take 3 deep long breaths in the nose & out of the mouth.

Center yourself in this thought/knowing that
"Everything is always working out for me."

Finish this sentence:

_____ I am so proud of you. Today you...
Your Name

_____

_____

Happy _____ Today is My Day!
(day of the week)

┌─ Today I feel: ─┐ ┌─ Today I want to feel: ─┐

I am grateful for, excited about, appreciative of, looking forward to:

1. _____

2. _____

3. _____

Morning Mantra:

Today is my day. I am in abundance. I have everything I need inside of me to Make Amazing Shit Happen. Everything is always working out for me. I am whole and complete. I look forward to GOD moving the universe on my behalf. I said it is so and so it is.

I will take the actions below in order to reach my desired feeling for today. I will practice in my good and better serving feeling as often as I need to or desire to today. I am committed to reaching and maintaining my desired feeling today.

1. _____

2. _____

3. _____

My intention for today is:

_____

_____

_____

_____

NIGHT TIME RELAX AND RELEASE SESSION

How was your day? **Rate your day**

| Amazing | Great | Good | OK | Bad | Terrible | It Sucked |

I am grateful for, glad about, appreciative of, looking forward to:

1. _____

2. _____

3. _____

Reflection:

What did today teach you?

_____
_____
_____

What are you releasing from today?

_____
_____
_____

_____ I see you & I hear you.
Your Name

Take 3 deep long breaths in the nose & out of the mouth.

Center yourself in this thought/knowing that
"Everything is always working out for me."

Finish this sentence:

_____ I am so proud of you. Today you...
Your Name

_____
_____

Happy _____ *Today is My Day!*
(day of the week)

┌─── *Today I feel:* ───┐ ┌─── *Today I want to feel:* ───┐

I am grateful for, excited about, appreciative of, looking forward to:

1. _____

2. _____

3. _____

Morning Mantra:

Today is my day. I am in abundance. I have everything I need inside of me to Make Amazing Shit Happen. Everything is always working out for me. I am whole and complete. I look forward to GOD moving the universe on my behalf. I said it is so and so it is.

I will take the actions below in order to reach my desired feeling for today. I will practice in my good and better serving feeling as often as I need to or desire to today. I am committed to reaching and maintaining my desired feeling today.

1. _____

2. _____

3. _____

My intention for today is:

_____
_____
_____
_____

How was your day? **Rate your day**

Amazing   Great   Good   OK   Bad   Terrible   It Sucked

I am grateful for, glad about, appreciative of, looking forward to:

1. _____

2. _____

3. _____

Reflection:

What did today teach you?

_____
_____
_____

What are you releasing from today?

_____
_____
_____

_____ I see you & I hear you.
Your Name

Take 3 deep long breaths in the nose & out of the mouth.

Center yourself in this thought/knowing that
"Everything is always working out for me."

Finish this sentence:

_____ I am so proud of you. Today you...
Your Name

_____
_____

Happy _____ *Today is My Day!*
(day of the week)

Today I feel:	*Today I want to feel:*

I am grateful for, excited about, appreciative of, looking forward to:

1. _____

2. _____

3. _____

Morning Mantra:

Today is my day. I am in abundance. I have everything I need inside of me to Make Amazing Shit Happen. Everything is always working out for me. I am whole and complete. I look forward to GOD moving the universe on my behalf. I said it is so and so it is.

I will take the actions below in order to reach my desired feeling for today. I will practice in my good and better serving feeling as often as I need to or desire to today. I am committed to reaching and maintaining my desired feeling today.

1. _____

2. _____

3. _____

My intention for today is:

_____

_____

_____

_____

NIGHT TIME RELAX AND RELEASE SESSION

How was your day? **Rate your day**

:-D	:-|	:-)	:-)	:-(	:-(	>:<
Amazing	Great	Good	OK	Bad	Terrible	It Sucked

I am grateful for, glad about, appreciative of, looking forward to:

1. _____

2. _____

3. _____

Reflection:

What did today teach you?

_____
_____
_____

What are you releasing from today?

_____
_____
_____

_____ I see you & I hear you.
Your Name

Take 3 deep long breaths in the nose & out of the mouth.

Center yourself in this thought/knowing that
"Everything is always working out for me."

Finish this sentence:

_____ I am so proud of you. Today you...
Your Name

_____
_____

Happy _____ *Today is My Day!*
(day of the week)

┌─── *Today I feel:* ───┐   ┌─── *Today I want to feel:* ───┐

I am grateful for, excited about, appreciative of, looking forward to:

1. _____

2. _____

3. _____

Morning Mantra:

Today is my day. I am in abundance. I have everything I need inside of me to Make Amazing Shit Happen. Everything is always working out for me. I am whole and complete. I look forward to GOD moving the universe on my behalf. I said it is so and so it is.

I will take the actions below in order to reach my desired feeling for today. I will practice in my good and better serving feeling as often as I need to or desire to today. I am committed to reaching and maintaining my desired feeling today.

1. _____

2. _____

3. _____

My intention for today is:

_____
_____
_____
_____

How was your day? **Rate your day**

Amazing   Great   Good   OK   Bad   Terrible   It Sucked

I am grateful for, glad about, appreciative of, looking forward to:

1. _____

2. _____

3. _____

Reflection:

What did today teach you?

_____
_____
_____

What are you releasing from today?

_____
_____
_____

_____ I see you & I hear you.
Your Name

Take 3 deep long breaths in the nose & out of the mouth.

Center yourself in this thought/knowing that
"Everything is always working out for me."

Finish this sentence:

_____ I am so proud of you. Today you...
Your Name

_____
_____

MORNING MINDSET SESSION

Happy _____
(day of the week)

Today is My Day!

┌─ Today I feel: ─┐   ┌─ Today I want to feel: ─┐
│   │   │   │
│   │   │   │
│   │   │   │
└─────────────────┘   └─────────────────────────┘

I am grateful for, excited about, appreciative of, looking forward to:

1. _____

2. _____

3. _____

Morning Mantra:

Today is my day. I am in abundance. I have everything I need inside of me to Make Amazing Shit Happen. Everything is always working out for me. I am whole and complete. I look forward to GOD moving the universe on my behalf. I said it is so and so it is.

I will take the actions below in order to reach my desired feeling for today. I will practice in my good and better serving feeling as often as I need to or desire to today. I am committed to reaching and maintaining my desired feeling today.

1. _____

2. _____

3. _____

My intention for today is:

_____
_____
_____
_____

NIGHT TIME RELAX AND RELEASE SESSION

How was your day? Rate your day

😄 Amazing   😬 Great   🙂 Good   🙂 OK   ☹️ Bad   😧 Terrible   😣 It Sucked

I am grateful for, glad about, appreciative of, looking forward to:

1. _____

2. _____

3. _____

Reflection:

What did today teach you?

_____
_____
_____

What are you releasing from today?

_____
_____
_____

_____ I see you & I hear you.
Your Name

Take 3 deep long breaths in the nose & out of the mouth.

Center yourself in this thought/knowing that
"Everything is always working out for me."

Finish this sentence:

_____ I am so proud of you. Today you...
Your Name

_____
_____

Happy _____ *Today is My Day!*
(day of the week)

┌─── *Today I feel:* ───┐   ┌─── *Today I want to feel:* ───┐
│   │   │   │
│   │   │   │
│   │   │   │
│   │   │   │
└──────────────────────┘   └───────────────────────────────┘

I am grateful for, excited about, appreciative of, looking forward to:

1. _____

2. _____

3. _____

Morning Mantra:

Today is my day. I am in abundance. I have everything I need inside of me to Make Amazing Shit Happen. Everything is always working out for me. I am whole and complete. I look forward to GOD moving the universe on my behalf. I said it is so and so it is.

I will take the actions below in order to reach my desired feeling for today. I will practice in my good and better serving feeling as often as I need to or desire to today. I am committed to reaching and maintaining my desired feeling today.

1. _____

2. _____

3. _____

My intention for today is:

_____
_____
_____
_____

How was your day? **Rate your day**

Amazing	Great	Good	OK	Bad	Terrible	It Sucked

I am grateful for, glad about, appreciative of, looking forward to:

1. _____

2. _____

3. _____

Reflection:

What did today teach you?

_____
_____
_____

What are you releasing from today?

_____
_____
_____

_____ I see you & I hear you.
Your Name

Take 3 deep long breaths in the nose & out of the mouth.

Center yourself in this thought/knowing that
"Everything is always working out for me."

Finish this sentence:

_____ I am so proud of you. Today you...
Your Name

_____
_____

Happy _____ _Today is My Day!_
(day of the week)

┌─ _Today I feel:_ ─┐   ┌─ _Today I want to feel:_ ─┐

I am grateful for, excited about, appreciative of, looking forward to:

1. _____

2. _____

3. _____

Morning Mantra:

Today is my day. I am in abundance. I have everything I need inside of me to Make Amazing Shit Happen. Everything is always working out for me. I am whole and complete. I look forward to GOD moving the universe on my behalf. I said it is so and so it is.

I will take the actions below in order to reach my desired feeling for today. I will practice in my good and better serving feeling as often as I need to or desire to today. I am committed to reaching and maintaining my desired feeling today.

1. _____

2. _____

3. _____

My intention for today is:

_____
_____
_____
_____

NIGHT TIME RELAX AND RELEASE SESSION

How was your day? **Rate your day**

😁   😐   🙂   🙂   🙁   😧   😖

Amazing   Great   Good   OK   Bad   Terrible   It Sucked

I am grateful for, glad about, appreciative of, looking forward to:

1. _____

2. _____

3. _____

Reflection:

What did today teach you?

_____

_____

_____

What are you releasing from today?

_____

_____

_____

_____ I see you & I hear you.
Your Name

Take 3 deep long breaths in the nose & out of the mouth.

Center yourself in this thought/knowing that
"Everything is always working out for me."

Finish this sentence:

_____ I am so proud of you. Today you...
Your Name

_____

_____

Happy _____ Today is My Day!
(day of the week)

┌─── Today I feel: ───┐   ┌─ Today I want to feel: ─┐

I am grateful for, excited about, appreciative of, looking forward to:

1. _____

2. _____

3. _____

Morning Mantra:

Today is my day. I am in abundance. I have everything I need inside of me to Make Amazing Shit Happen. Everything is always working out for me. I am whole and complete. I look forward to GOD moving the universe on my behalf. I said it is so and so it is.

I will take the actions below in order to reach my desired feeling for today. I will practice in my good and better serving feeling as often as I need to or desire to today. I am committed to reaching and maintaining my desired feeling today.

1. _____

2. _____

3. _____

My intention for today is:

_____
_____
_____
_____

How was your day? **Rate your day**

😃	😐	🙂	🙂	🙁	😧	😣
Amazing	Great	Good	OK	Bad	Terrible	It Sucked

I am grateful for, glad about, appreciative of, looking forward to:

1. _____

2. _____

3. _____

Reflection:

What did today teach you?

_____
_____
_____

What are you releasing from today?

_____
_____
_____

_____ I see you & I hear you.
Your Name

Take 3 deep long breaths in the nose & out of the mouth.

Center yourself in this thought/knowing that
"Everything is always working out for me."

Finish this sentence:

_____ I am so proud of you. Today you...
Your Name

_____
_____

MORNING MINDSET SESSION

Happy _____ *Today is My Day!*
(day of the week)

Today I feel:

Today I want to feel:

I am grateful for, excited about, appreciative of, looking forward to:

1. _____

2. _____

3. _____

Morning Mantra:

Today is my day. I am in abundance. I have everything I need inside of me to Make Amazing Shit Happen. Everything is always working out for me. I am whole and complete. I look forward to GOD moving the universe on my behalf. I said it is so and so it is.

I will take the actions below in order to reach my desired feeling for today. I will practice in my good and better serving feeling as often as I need to or desire to today. I am committed to reaching and maintaining my desired feeling today.

1. _____

2. _____

3. _____

My intention for today is:

_____
_____
_____
_____

NIGHT TIME RELAX AND RELEASE SESSION

How was your day? **Rate your day**

😀 Amazing   😐 Great   🙂 Good   🙂 OK   🙁 Bad   😧 Terrible   😣 It Sucked

I am grateful for, glad about, appreciative of, looking forward to:

1. _____

2. _____

3. _____

Reflection:

What did today teach you?

_____
_____
_____

What are you releasing from today?

_____
_____
_____

_____ I see you & I hear you.
Your Name

Take 3 deep long breaths in the nose & out of the mouth.

Center yourself in this thought/knowing that
"Everything is always working out for me."

Finish this sentence:

_____ I am so proud of you. Today you...
Your Name

_____
_____

Happy _____ *Today is My Day!*
(day of the week)

Today I feel:

Today I want to feel:

I am grateful for, excited about, appreciative of, looking forward to:

1. _____

2. _____

3. _____

Morning Mantra:

Today is my day. I am in abundance. I have everything I need inside of me to Make Amazing Shit Happen. Everything is always working out for me. I am whole and complete. I look forward to GOD moving the universe on my behalf. I said it is so and so it is.

I will take the actions below in order to reach my desired feeling for today. I will practice in my good and better serving feeling as often as I need to or desire to today. I am committed to reaching and maintaining my desired feeling today.

1. _____

2. _____

3. _____

My intention for today is:

_____
_____
_____
_____
_____

How was your day? **Rate your day**

| Amazing | Great | Good | OK | Bad | Terrible | It Sucked |

I am grateful for, glad about, appreciative of, looking forward to:

1. _____

2. _____

3. _____

Reflection:

What did today teach you?

_____

_____

_____

What are you releasing from today?

_____

_____

_____

_____ I see you & I hear you.
Your Name

Take 3 deep long breaths in the nose & out of the mouth.

Center yourself in this thought/knowing that
"Everything is always working out for me."

Finish this sentence:

_____ I am so proud of you. Today you...
Your Name

_____

_____

MORNING MINDSET SESSION

Happy _____ *Today is My Day!*
(day of the week)

┌─── *Today I feel:* ───┐   ┌─── *Today I want to feel:* ───┐
│   │   │   │
│   │   │   │
│   │   │   │
│   │   │   │
└───────────────────────┘   └────────────────────────────────┘

I am grateful for, excited about, appreciative of, looking forward to:

1. _____

2. _____

3. _____

Morning Mantra:

Today is my day. I am in abundance. I have everything I need inside of me to Make Amazing Shit Happen. Everything is always working out for me. I am whole and complete. I look forward to GOD moving the universe on my behalf. I said it is so and so it is.

I will take the actions below in order to reach my desired feeling for today. I will practice in my good and better serving feeling as often as I need to or desire to today. I am committed to reaching and maintaining my desired feeling today.

1. _____

2. _____

3. _____

My intention for today is:

_____
_____
_____
_____

NIGHT TIME RELAX AND RELEASE SESSION

How was your day? **Rate your day**

Amazing   Great   Good   OK   Bad   Terrible   It Sucked

I am grateful for, glad about, appreciative of, looking forward to:

1. _____

2. _____

3. _____

Reflection:

What did today teach you?

_____
_____
_____

What are you releasing from today?

_____
_____
_____

_____ I see you & I hear you.
Your Name

Take 3 deep long breaths in the nose & out of the mouth.

Center yourself in this thought/knowing that
"Everything is always working out for me."

Finish this sentence:

_____ I am so proud of you. Today you...
Your Name

_____
_____

Happy _____ Today is My Day!
(day of the week)

┌─ Today I feel: ─┐ ┌─ Today I want to feel: ─┐

I am grateful for, excited about, appreciative of, looking forward to:

1. _____

2. _____

3. _____

Morning Mantra:

Today is my day. I am in abundance. I have everything I need inside of me to Make Amazing Shit Happen. Everything is always working out for me. I am whole and complete. I look forward to GOD moving the universe on my behalf. I said it is so and so it is.

I will take the actions below in order to reach my desired feeling for today. I will practice in my good and better serving feeling as often as I need to or desire to today. I am committed to reaching and maintaining my desired feeling today.

1. _____

2. _____

3. _____

My intention for today is:

_____
_____
_____
_____

How was your day? **Rate your day**

:)	:|	:)	:)	:(	:(	><
Amazing	Great	Good	OK	Bad	Terrible	It Sucked

I am grateful for, glad about, appreciative of, looking forward to:

1. _____

2. _____

3. _____

Reflection:

What did today teach you?

_____

_____

_____

What are you releasing from today?

_____

_____

_____

_____

_____ I see you & I hear you.
Your Name

Take 3 deep long breaths in the nose & out of the mouth.

Center yourself in this thought/knowing that
"Everything is always working out for me."

Finish this sentence:

_____ I am so proud of you. Today you...
Your Name

_____

_____

MORNING MINDSET SESSION

Happy _____   *Today is My Day!*
(day of the week)

Today I feel:	*Today I want to feel:*

I am grateful for, excited about, appreciative of, looking forward to:

1. _____

2. _____

3. _____

Morning Mantra:

Today is my day. I am in abundance. I have everything I need inside of me to Make Amazing Shit Happen. Everything is always working out for me. I am whole and complete. I look forward to GOD moving the universe on my behalf. I said it is so and so it is.

I will take the actions below in order to reach my desired feeling for today. I will practice in my good and better serving feeling as often as I need to or desire to today. I am committed to reaching and maintaining my desired feeling today.

1. _____

2. _____

3. _____

My intention for today is:

_____

_____

_____

_____

NIGHT TIME RELAX AND RELEASE SESSION

How was your day? **Rate your day**

| Amazing | Great | Good | OK | Bad | Terrible | It Sucked |

I am grateful for, glad about, appreciative of, looking forward to:

1. _____

2. _____

3. _____

Reflection:

What did today teach you?

_____
_____
_____

What are you releasing from today?

_____
_____
_____

_____ I see you & I hear you.
                Your Name

Take 3 deep long breaths in the nose & out of the mouth.

Center yourself in this thought/knowing that
"Everything is always working out for me."

Finish this sentence:

_____ I am so proud of you. Today you...
        Your Name

_____
_____

Happy _____ *Today is My Day!*
(day of the week)

┌─ *Today I feel:* ─┐   ┌─ *Today I want to feel:* ─┐

I am grateful for, excited about, appreciative of, looking forward to:

1. _____

2. _____

3. _____

Morning Mantra:

Today is my day. I am in abundance. I have everything I need inside of me to Make Amazing Shit Happen. Everything is always working out for me. I am whole and complete. I look forward to GOD moving the universe on my behalf. I said it is so and so it is.

I will take the actions below in order to reach my desired feeling for today. I will practice in my good and better serving feeling as often as I need to or desire to today. I am committed to reaching and maintaining my desired feeling today.

1. _____

2. _____

3. _____

My intention for today is:

_____

_____

_____

_____

How was your day? **Rate your day**

😃	😑	🙂	🙂	🙁	😟	😣
Amazing	Great	Good	OK	Bad	Terrible	It Sucked

I am grateful for, glad about, appreciative of, looking forward to:

1. _____

2. _____

3. _____

Reflection:

What did today teach you?

_____
_____
_____

What are you releasing from today?

_____
_____
_____

_____ I see you & I hear you.
Your Name

Take 3 deep long breaths in the nose & out of the mouth.

Center yourself in this thought/knowing that
"Everything is always working out for me."

Finish this sentence:

_____ I am so proud of you. Today you...
Your Name

_____
_____

MORNING MINDSET SESSION

Happy _____
(day of the week)

Today is My Day!

┌─── Today I feel: ───┐   ┌─── Today I want to feel: ───┐

I am grateful for, excited about, appreciative of, looking forward to:

1. _____

2. _____

3. _____

Morning Mantra:

Today is my day. I am in abundance. I have everything I need inside of me to Make Amazing Shit Happen. Everything is always working out for me. I am whole and complete. I look forward to GOD moving the universe on my behalf. I said it is so and so it is.

I will take the actions below in order to reach my desired feeling for today. I will practice in my good and better serving feeling as often as I need to or desire to to-day. I am committed to reaching and maintaining my desired feeling today.

1. _____

2. _____

3. _____

My intention for today is:

_____
_____
_____
_____

NIGHT TIME RELAX AND RELEASE SESSION

How was your day? **Rate your day**

:-D	:-|	:-)	:-)	:-(	:-(	>:<
Amazing	Great	Good	OK	Bad	Terrible	It Sucked

I am grateful for, glad about, appreciative of, looking forward to:

1. _____

2. _____

3. _____

Reflection:

What did today teach you?

_____
_____
_____

What are you releasing from today?

_____
_____
_____

_____ I see you & I hear you.
Your Name

Take 3 deep long breaths in the nose & out of the mouth.

Center yourself in this thought/knowing that
"Everything is always working out for me."

Finish this sentence:

_____ I am so proud of you. Today you...
Your Name

_____
_____

Happy _____ *Today is My Day!*
(day of the week)

┌─ *Today I feel:* ─┐   ┌─ *Today I want to feel:* ─┐

I am grateful for, excited about, appreciative of, looking forward to:

1. _____

2. _____

3. _____

Morning Mantra:

Today is my day. I am in abundance. I have everything I need inside of me to Make Amazing Shit Happen. Everything is always working out for me. I am whole and complete. I look forward to GOD moving the universe on my behalf. I said it is so and so it is.

I will take the actions below in order to reach my desired feeling for today. I will practice in my good and better serving feeling as often as I need to or desire to today. I am committed to reaching and maintaining my desired feeling today.

1. _____

2. _____

3. _____

My intention for today is:

_____
_____
_____
_____

How was your day? **Rate your day**

Amazing	Great	Good	OK	Bad	Terrible	It Sucked

I am grateful for, glad about, appreciative of, looking forward to:

1. _____

2. _____

3. _____

Reflection:

What did today teach you?

_____
_____
_____

What are you releasing from today?

_____
_____
_____

_____ I see you & I hear you.
Your Name

Take 3 deep long breaths in the nose & out of the mouth.

Center yourself in this thought/knowing that
"Everything is always working out for me."

Finish this sentence:

_____ I am so proud of you. Today you...
Your Name

_____
_____

MORNING MINDSET SESSION

Happy _____
(day of the week)

Today is My Day!

┌─── Today I feel: ───┐   ┌─── Today I want to feel: ───┐

I am grateful for, excited about, appreciative of, looking forward to:

1. _____

2. _____

3. _____

Morning Mantra:

Today is my day. I am in abundance. I have everything I need inside of me to Make Amazing Shit Happen. Everything is always working out for me. I am whole and complete. I look forward to GOD moving the universe on my behalf. I said it is so and so it is.

I will take the actions below in order to reach my desired feeling for today. I will practice in my good and better serving feeling as often as I need to or desire to today. I am committed to reaching and maintaining my desired feeling today.

1. _____

2. _____

3. _____

My intention for today is:

_____
_____
_____
_____

NIGHT TIME RELAX AND RELEASE SESSION

How was your day? **Rate your day**

Amazing	Great	Good	OK	Bad	Terrible	It Sucked

I am grateful for, glad about, appreciative of, looking forward to:

1. _____

2. _____

3. _____

Reflection:

What did today teach you?

_____

_____

_____

What are you releasing from today?

_____

_____

_____

_____ I see you & I hear you.
Your Name

Take 3 deep long breaths in the nose & out of the mouth.

Center yourself in this thought/knowing that
"Everything is always working out for me."

Finish this sentence:

_____ I am so proud of you. Today you...
Your Name

_____

_____

Happy _____ *Today is My Day!*
(day of the week)

┌─── *Today I feel:* ───┐   ┌─── *Today I want to feel:* ───┐
│   │   │   │
│   │   │   │
│   │   │   │
│   │   │   │
│   │   │   │
└───────────────────────┘   └────────────────────────────────┘

I am grateful for, excited about, appreciative of, looking forward to:

1. _____

2. _____

3. _____

Morning Mantra:

Today is my day. I am in abundance. I have everything I need inside of me to Make Amazing Shit Happen. Everything is always working out for me. I am whole and complete. I look forward to GOD moving the universe on my behalf. I said it is so and so it is.

I will take the actions below in order to reach my desired feeling for today. I will practice in my good and better serving feeling as often as I need to or desire to to-day. I am committed to reaching and maintaining my desired feeling today.

1. _____

2. _____

3. _____

My intention for today is:

_____
_____
_____
_____
_____

How was your day? Rate your day

Amazing	Great	Good	OK	Bad	Terrible	It Sucked

I am grateful for, glad about, appreciative of, looking forward to:

1. _____

2. _____

3. _____

Reflection:

What did today teach you?

_____

_____

_____

What are you releasing from today?

_____

_____

_____

_____ I see you & I hear you.
Your Name

Take 3 deep long breaths in the nose & out of the mouth.

Center yourself in this thought/knowing that
"Everything is always working out for me."

Finish this sentence:

_____ I am so proud of you. Today you...
Your Name

_____

_____

MORNING MINDSET SESSION

Happy _____   Today is My Day!
(day of the week)

┌─ Today I feel: ─┐   ┌─ Today I want to feel: ─┐

I am grateful for, excited about, appreciative of, looking forward to:

1. _____

2. _____

3. _____

Morning Mantra:

Today is my day. I am in abundance. I have everything I need inside of me to Make Amazing Shit Happen. Everything is always working out for me. I am whole and complete. I look forward to GOD moving the universe on my behalf. I said it is so and so it is.

I will take the actions below in order to reach my desired feeling for today. I will practice in my good and better serving feeling as often as I need to or desire to today. I am committed to reaching and maintaining my desired feeling today.

1. _____

2. _____

3. _____

My intention for today is:

_____
_____
_____
_____

NIGHT TIME RELAX AND RELEASE SESSION

How was your day? **Rate your day**

Amazing   Great   Good   OK   Bad   Terrible   It Sucked

am grateful for, glad about, appreciative of, looking forward to:

1. _____

2. _____

3. _____

Reflection:

What did today teach you?

_____
_____
_____

What are you releasing from today?

_____
_____
_____

_____ I see you & I hear you.
Your Name

Take 3 deep long breaths in the nose & out of the mouth.

Center yourself in this thought/knowing that
"Everything is always working out for me."

Finish this sentence:

_____ I am so proud of you. Today you...
Your Name

_____
_____

Happy _____ *Today is My Day!*
(day of the week)

┌─ *Today I feel:* ─┐   ┌─ *Today I want to feel:* ─┐
│   │   │   │
│   │   │   │
│   │   │   │
│   │   │   │
└───────────────────┘   └───────────────────────────┘

I am grateful for, excited about, appreciative of, looking forward to:

1. _____

2. _____

3. _____

Morning Mantra:

Today is my day. I am in abundance. I have everything I need inside of me to Make Amazing Shit Happen. Everything is always working out for me. I am whole and complete. I look forward to GOD moving the universe on my behalf. I said it is so and so it is.

I will take the actions below in order to reach my desired feeling for today. I will practice in my good and better serving feeling as often as I need to or desire to today. I am committed to reaching and maintaining my desired feeling today.

1. _____

2. _____

3. _____

My intention for today is:

_____
_____
_____
_____

How was your day? **Rate your day**

:)	:|	:)	:)	:(	:(	><
Amazing	Great	Good	OK	Bad	Terrible	It Sucked

I am grateful for, glad about, appreciative of, looking forward to:

1. _____

2. _____

3. _____

Reflection:

What did today teach you?

_____

_____

_____

What are you releasing from today?

_____

_____

_____

_____ I see you & I hear you.
Your Name

Take 3 deep long breaths in the nose & out of the mouth.

Center yourself in this thought/knowing that
"Everything is always working out for me."

Finish this sentence:

_____ I am so proud of you. Today you...
Your Name

_____

_____

MORNING MINDSET SESSION

Happy _____
(day of the week)

Today is My Day!

┌─── Today I feel: ───┐   ┌─── Today I want to feel: ───┐

I am grateful for, excited about, appreciative of, looking forward to:

1. _____

2. _____

3. _____

Morning Mantra:

Today is my day. I am in abundance. I have everything I need inside of me to Make Amazing Shit Happen. Everything is always working out for me. I am whole and complete. I look forward to GOD moving the universe on my behalf. I said it is so and so it is.

I will take the actions below in order to reach my desired feeling for today. I will practice in my good and better serving feeling as often as I need to or desire to today. I am committed to reaching and maintaining my desired feeling today.

1. _____

2. _____

3. _____

My intention for today is:

_____
_____
_____
_____

NIGHT TIME RELAX AND RELEASE SESSION

How was your day? **Rate your day**

Amazing	Great	Good	OK	Bad	Terrible	It Sucked

I am grateful for, glad about, appreciative of, looking forward to:

1. _____

2. _____

3. _____

Reflection:

What did today teach you?

_____

_____

_____

What are you releasing from today?

_____

_____

_____

_____ I see you & I hear you.
Your Name

Take 3 deep long breaths in the nose & out of the mouth.

Center yourself in this thought/knowing that
"Everything is always working out for me."

Finish this sentence:

_____ I am so proud of you. Today you...
Your Name

_____

_____

Happy _____ Today is My Day!
(day of the week)

┌─ Today I feel: ─┐   ┌─ Today I want to feel: ─┐

I am grateful for, excited about, appreciative of, looking forward to:

1. _____

2. _____

3. _____

Morning Mantra:

Today is my day. I am in abundance. I have everything I need inside of me to Make Amazing Shit Happen. Everything is always working out for me. I am whole and complete. I look forward to GOD moving the universe on my behalf. I said it is so and so it is.

I will take the actions below in order to reach my desired feeling for today. I will practice in my good and better serving feeling as often as I need to or desire to today. I am committed to reaching and maintaining my desired feeling today.

1. _____

2. _____

3. _____

My intention for today is:

_____
_____
_____
_____

How was your day? **Rate your day**

Amazing	Great	Good	OK	Bad	Terrible	It Sucked

I am grateful for, glad about, appreciative of, looking forward to:

1. _____

2. _____

3. _____

Reflection:

What did today teach you?

_____
_____
_____

What are you releasing from today?

_____
_____
_____

_____ I see you & I hear you.
Your Name

Take 3 deep long breaths in the nose & out of the mouth.

Center yourself in this thought/knowing that
"Everything is always working out for me."

Finish this sentence:

_____ I am so proud of you. Today you...
Your Name

_____
_____

Happy _____ Today is My Day!
(day of the week)

┌─────────────────┐   ┌─────────────────┐
│ Today I feel: │   │ Today I want to feel: │
│   │   │   │
│   │   │   │
└─────────────────┘   └─────────────────┘

I am grateful for, excited about, appreciative of, looking forward to:

1. _____

2. _____

3. _____

Morning Mantra:

Today is my day. I am in abundance. I have everything I need inside of me to Make Amazing Shit Happen. Everything is always working out for me. I am whole and complete. I look forward to GOD moving the universe on my behalf. I said it is so and so it is.

I will take the actions below in order to reach my desired feeling for today. I will practice in my good and better serving feeling as often as I need to or desire to today. I am committed to reaching and maintaining my desired feeling today.

1. _____

2. _____

3. _____

My intention for today is:

_____
_____
_____
_____

NIGHT TIME RELAX AND RELEASE SESSION

How was your day? **Rate your day**

| Amazing | Great | Good | OK | Bad | Terrible | It Sucked |

I am grateful for, glad about, appreciative of, looking forward to:

1. _____

2. _____

3. _____

Reflection:

What did today teach you?

_____
_____
_____

What are you releasing from today?

_____
_____
_____

_____ I see you & I hear you.
Your Name

Take 3 deep long breaths in the nose & out of the mouth.

Center yourself in this thought/knowing that
"Everything is always working out for me."

Finish this sentence:

_____ I am so proud of you. Today you...
Your Name

_____
_____

Happy _____ *Today is My Day!*
(day of the week)

┌─ *Today I feel:* ─┐   ┌─ *Today I want to feel:* ─┐

I am grateful for, excited about, appreciative of, looking forward to:

1. _____

2. _____

3. _____

Morning Mantra:

Today is my day. I am in abundance. I have everything I need inside of me to Make Amazing Shit Happen. Everything is always working out for me. I am whole and complete. I look forward to GOD moving the universe on my behalf. I said it is so and so it is.

I will take the actions below in order to reach my desired feeling for today. I will practice in my good and better serving feeling as often as I need to or desire to today. I am committed to reaching and maintaining my desired feeling today.

1. _____

2. _____

3. _____

My intention for today is:

_____
_____
_____
_____

How was your day? Rate your day

| Amazing | Great | Good | OK | Bad | Terrible | It Sucked |

I am grateful for, glad about, appreciative of, looking forward to:

1. _____

2. _____

3. _____

Reflection:

What did today teach you?

_____
_____
_____

What are you releasing from today?

_____
_____
_____

_____ I see you & I hear you.
Your Name

Take 3 deep long breaths in the nose & out of the mouth.

Center yourself in this thought/knowing that
"Everything is always working out for me."

Finish this sentence:

_____ I am so proud of you. Today you...
Your Name

_____
_____

MORNING MINDSET SESSION

Happy _____
(day of the week)

Today is My Day!

┌─── Today I feel: ───┐   ┌─── Today I want to feel: ───┐

I am grateful for, excited about, appreciative of, looking forward to:

1. _____

2. _____

3. _____

Morning Mantra:

Today is my day. I am in abundance. I have everything I need inside of me to Make Amazing Shit Happen. Everything is always working out for me. I am whole and complete. I look forward to GOD moving the universe on my behalf. I said it is so and so it is.

I will take the actions below in order to reach my desired feeling for today. I will practice in my good and better serving feeling as often as I need to or desire to today. I am committed to reaching and maintaining my desired feeling today.

1. _____

2. _____

3. _____

My intention for today is:

_____
_____
_____
_____

NIGHT TIME RELAX AND RELEASE SESSION

How was your day? **Rate your day**

:D   :| :)   :)   :(:(>.<
Amazing   Great   Good   OK   Bad   Terrible   It Sucked

I am grateful for, glad about, appreciative of, looking forward to:

1. _____

2. _____

3. _____

Reflection:

What did today teach you?

_____
_____
_____

What are you releasing from today?

_____
_____
_____

_____ I see you & I hear you.
Your Name

Take 3 deep long breaths in the nose & out of the mouth.

Center yourself in this thought/knowing that
"Everything is always working out for me."

Finish this sentence:

_____ I am so proud of you. Today you...
Your Name

_____
_____

Happy _____
(day of the week)

Today is My Day!

┌─ Today I feel: ─┐   ┌─ Today I want to feel: ─┐
│   │   │   │
│   │   │   │
│   │   │   │
└─────────────────┘   └─────────────────────────┘

I am grateful for, excited about, appreciative of, looking forward to:

1. _____

2. _____

3. _____

Morning Mantra:

Today is my day. I am in abundance. I have everything I need inside of me to Make Amazing Shit Happen. Everything is always working out for me. I am whole and complete. I look forward to GOD moving the universe on my behalf. I said it is so and so it is.

I will take the actions below in order to reach my desired feeling for today. I will practice in my good and better serving feeling as often as I need to or desire to today. I am committed to reaching and maintaining my desired feeling today.

1. _____

2. _____

3. _____

My intention for today is:

_____
_____
_____
_____

NIGHT TIME RELAX AND RELEASE SESSION

How was your day? **Rate your day**

😃 😬 🙂 🙂 🙁 😟 😖
Amazing   Great   Good   OK   Bad   Terrible   It Sucked

I am grateful for, glad about, appreciative of, looking forward to:

1. _____

2. _____

3. _____

Reflection:

What did today teach you?

_____
_____
_____

What are you releasing from today?

_____
_____
_____

_____ I see you & I hear you.
Your Name

Take 3 deep long breaths in the nose & out of the mouth.

Center yourself in this thought/knowing that
"Everything is always working out for me."

Finish this sentence:

_____ I am so proud of you. Today you...
Your Name

_____
_____

MORNING MINDSET SESSION

Happy _____   Today is My Day!
(day of the week)

┌─── Today I feel: ───┐ ┌─── Today I want to feel: ───┐
│   │ │   │
│   │ │   │
│   │ │   │
│   │ │   │
└─────────────────────┘ └─────────────────────────────┘

I am grateful for, excited about, appreciative of, looking forward to:

1. _____

2. _____

3. _____

Morning Mantra:

Today is my day. I am in abundance. I have everything I need inside of me to Make Amazing Shit Happen. Everything is always working out for me. I am whole and complete. I look forward to GOD moving the universe on my behalf. I said it is so and so it is.

I will take the actions below in order to reach my desired feeling for today. I will practice in my good and better serving feeling as often as I need to or desire to today. I am committed to reaching and maintaining my desired feeling today.

1. _____

2. _____

3. _____

My intention for today is:

_____
_____
_____
_____

NIGHT TIME RELAX AND RELEASE SESSION

How was your day? **Rate your day**

😄 😐 🙂 🙂 🙁 ☹️ 😣
Amazing Great Good OK Bad Terrible It Sucked

I am grateful for, glad about, appreciative of, looking forward to:

1. _____

2. _____

3. _____

Reflection:

What did today teach you?

_____
_____
_____

What are you releasing from today?

_____
_____
_____

_____ I see you & I hear you.
Your Name

Take 3 deep long breaths in the nose & out of the mouth.

Center yourself in this thought/knowing that
"Everything is always working out for me."

Finish this sentence:

_____ I am so proud of you. Today you...
Your Name

_____
_____

Happy _____ *Today is My Day!*
(day of the week)

┌─── *Today I feel:* ───┐   ┌─── *Today I want to feel:* ───┐
│   │   │   │
│   │   │   │
│   │   │   │
│   │   │   │
│   │   │   │
└───────────────────────┘   └────────────────────────────────┘

I am grateful for, excited about, appreciative of, looking forward to:

1. _____

2. _____

3. _____

Morning Mantra:

Today is my day. I am in abundance. I have everything I need inside of me to Make Amazing Shit Happen. Everything is always working out for me. I am whole and complete. I look forward to GOD moving the universe on my behalf. I said it is so and so it is.

I will take the actions below in order to reach my desired feeling for today. I will practice in my good and better serving feeling as often as I need to or desire to today. I am committed to reaching and maintaining my desired feeling today.

1. _____

2. _____

3. _____

My intention for today is:

_____
_____
_____
_____
_____

How was your day? **Rate your day**

😛 Amazing 😬 Great 😊 Good 🙂 OK 🙁 Bad 😣 Terrible 😆 It Sucked

I am grateful for, glad about, appreciative of, looking forward to:

1. _____

2. _____

3. _____

Reflection:

What did today teach you?

_____
_____
_____

What are you releasing from today?

_____
_____
_____

_____ I see you & I hear you.
Your Name

Take 3 deep long breaths in the nose & out of the mouth.

Center yourself in this thought/knowing that
"Everything is always working out for me."

Finish this sentence:

_____ I am so proud of you. Today you...
Your Name

_____
_____

Happy _____   *Today is My Day!*
(day of the week)

┌─── *Today I feel:* ───┐   ┌─ *Today I want to feel:* ─┐

I am grateful for, excited about, appreciative of, looking forward to:

1. _____

2. _____

3. _____

Morning Mantra:

Today is my day. I am in abundance. I have everything I need inside of me to Make Amazing Shit Happen. Everything is always working out for me. I am whole and complete. I look forward to GOD moving the universe on my behalf. I said it is so and so it is.

I will take the actions below in order to reach my desired feeling for today. I will practice in my good and better serving feeling as often as I need to or desire to today. I am committed to reaching and maintaining my desired feeling today.

1. _____

2. _____

3. _____

My intention for today is:

_____
_____
_____
_____

NIGHT TIME RELAX AND RELEASE SESSION

How was your day? **Rate your day**

Amazing   Great   Good   OK   Bad   Terrible   It Sucked

I am grateful for, glad about, appreciative of, looking forward to:

1. _____

2. _____

3. _____

Reflection:

What did today teach you?

_____
_____
_____

What are you releasing from today?

_____
_____
_____

_____ I see you & I hear you.
Your Name

Take 3 deep long breaths in the nose & out of the mouth.

Center yourself in this thought/knowing that
"Everything is always working out for me."

Finish this sentence:

_____ I am so proud of you. Today you...
Your Name

_____
_____

Happy _____ *Today is My Day!*
(day of the week)

┌─ *Today I feel:* ─┐   ┌─ *Today I want to feel:* ─┐

I am grateful for, excited about, appreciative of, looking forward to:

1. _____

2. _____

3. _____

Morning Mantra:

Today is my day. I am in abundance. I have everything I need inside of me to Make Amazing Shit Happen. Everything is always working out for me. I am whole and complete. I look forward to GOD moving the universe on my behalf. I said it is so and so it is.

I will take the actions below in order to reach my desired feeling for today. I will practice in my good and better serving feeling as often as I need to or desire to today. I am committed to reaching and maintaining my desired feeling today.

1. _____

2. _____

3. _____

My intention for today is:

_____
_____
_____
_____

How was your day? **Rate your day**

Amazing	Great	Good	OK	Bad	Terrible	It Sucked

I am grateful for, glad about, appreciative of, looking forward to:

1. _____

2. _____

3. _____

Reflection:

What did today teach you?

_____
_____
_____

What are you releasing from today?

_____
_____
_____

_____ I see you & I hear you.
Your Name

Take 3 deep long breaths in the nose & out of the mouth.

Center yourself in this thought/knowing that
"Everything is always working out for me."

Finish this sentence:

_____ I am so proud of you. Today you...
Your Name

_____
_____

Happy _____
(day of the week)

Today is My Day!

> *Today I feel:*

> *Today I want to feel:*

I am grateful for, excited about, appreciative of, looking forward to:

1. _____
2. _____
3. _____

Morning Mantra:

Today is my day. I am in abundance. I have everything I need inside of me to Make Amazing Shit Happen. Everything is always working out for me. I am whole and complete. I look forward to GOD moving the universe on my behalf. I said it is so and so it is.

I will take the actions below in order to reach my desired feeling for today. I will practice in my good and better serving feeling as often as I need to or desire to today. I am committed to reaching and maintaining my desired feeling today.

1. _____
2. _____
3. _____

My intention for today is:

_____
_____
_____
_____

NIGHT TIME RELAX AND RELEASE SESSION

How was your day? **Rate your day**

😃   😐   🙂   🙂   ☹️   😧   😖

Amazing   Great   Good   OK   Bad   Terrible   It Sucked

I am grateful for, glad about, appreciative of, looking forward to:

1. _____

2. _____

3. _____

Reflection:

What did today teach you?

_____
_____
_____

What are you releasing from today?

_____
_____
_____

_____ I see you & I hear you.
Your Name

Take 3 deep long breaths in the nose & out of the mouth.

Center yourself in this thought/knowing that
"Everything is always working out for me."

Finish this sentence:

_____ I am so proud of you. Today you...
Your Name

_____
_____

Happy _____   *Today is My Day!*
(day of the week)

┌─ *Today I feel:* ─┐   ┌─ *Today I want to feel:* ─┐

I am grateful for, excited about, appreciative of, looking forward to:

1. _____

2. _____

3. _____

Morning Mantra:

Today is my day. I am in abundance. I have everything I need inside of me to Make Amazing Shit Happen. Everything is always working out for me. I am whole and complete. I look forward to GOD moving the universe on my behalf. I said it is so and so it is.

I will take the actions below in order to reach my desired feeling for today. I will practice in my good and better serving feeling as often as I need to or desire to today. I am committed to reaching and maintaining my desired feeling today.

1. _____

2. _____

3. _____

My intention for today is:

_____
_____
_____
_____
_____

How was your day? **Rate your day**

| Amazing | Great | Good | OK | Bad | Terrible | It Sucked |

I am grateful for, glad about, appreciative of, looking forward to:

1. _____

2. _____

3. _____

Reflection:

What did today teach you?

_____
_____
_____

What are you releasing from today?

_____
_____
_____

_____ I see you & I hear you.
Your Name

Take 3 deep long breaths in the nose & out of the mouth.

Center yourself in this thought/knowing that
"Everything is always working out for me."

Finish this sentence:

_____ I am so proud of you. Today you...
Your Name

_____
_____

MORNING MINDSET SESSION

Happy _____ Today is My Day!
(day of the week)

┌─── Today I feel: ───┐ ┌─ Today I want to feel: ─┐
│   │ │   │
│   │ │   │
│   │ │   │
│   │ │   │
└─────────────────────┘ └─────────────────────────┘

I am grateful for, excited about, appreciative of, looking forward to:

1. _____

2. _____

3. _____

Morning Mantra:

Today is my day. I am in abundance. I have everything I need inside of me to Make Amazing Shit Happen. Everything is always working out for me. I am whole and complete. I look forward to GOD moving the universe on my behalf. I said it is so and so it is.

I will take the actions below in order to reach my desired feeling for today. I will practice in my good and better serving feeling as often as I need to or desire to today. I am committed to reaching and maintaining my desired feeling today.

1. _____

2. _____

3. _____

My intention for today is:

_____
_____
_____
_____

NIGHT TIME RELAX AND RELEASE SESSION

How was your day? **Rate your day**

| Amazing | Great | Good | OK | Bad | Terrible | It Sucked |

I am grateful for, glad about, appreciative of, looking forward to:

1. _____

2. _____

3. _____

Reflection:

What did today teach you?

_____
_____
_____

What are you releasing from today?

_____
_____
_____

_____ I see you & I hear you.
Your Name

Take 3 deep long breaths in the nose & out of the mouth.

Center yourself in this thought/knowing that
"Everything is always working out for me."

Finish this sentence:

_____ I am so proud of you. Today you...
Your Name

_____
_____

Happy _____ Today is My Day!
(day of the week)

┌─ Today I feel: ─┐   ┌─ Today I want to feel: ─┐

I am grateful for, excited about, appreciative of, looking forward to:

1. _____

2. _____

3. _____

Morning Mantra:

Today is my day. I am in abundance. I have everything I need inside of me to Make Amazing Shit Happen. Everything is always working out for me. I am whole and complete. I look forward to GOD moving the universe on my behalf. I said it is so and so it is.

I will take the actions below in order to reach my desired feeling for today. I will practice in my good and better serving feeling as often as I need to or desire to today. I am committed to reaching and maintaining my desired feeling today.

1. _____

2. _____

3. _____

My intention for today is:

_____
_____
_____
_____

How was your day? **Rate your day**

Amazing	Great	Good	OK	Bad	Terrible	It Sucked

I am grateful for, glad about, appreciative of, looking forward to:

1. _____

2. _____

3. _____

Reflection:

What did today teach you?

_____
_____
_____

What are you releasing from today?

_____
_____
_____

_____ I see you & I hear you.
Your Name

Take 3 deep long breaths in the nose & out of the mouth.

Center yourself in this thought/knowing that
"Everything is always working out for me."

Finish this sentence:

_____ I am so proud of you. Today you...
Your Name

_____
_____

Happy _____   *Today is My Day!*
(day of the week)

┌─ *Today I feel:* ─┐   ┌─ *Today I want to feel:* ─┐

I am grateful for, excited about, appreciative of, looking forward to:

1. _____

2. _____

3. _____

Morning Mantra:

Today is my day. I am in abundance. I have everything I need inside of me to Make Amazing Shit Happen. Everything is always working out for me. I am whole and complete. I look forward to GOD moving the universe on my behalf. I said it is so and so it is.

I will take the actions below in order to reach my desired feeling for today. I will practice in my good and better serving feeling as often as I need to or desire to to-day. I am committed to reaching and maintaining my desired feeling today.

1. _____

2. _____

3. _____

My intention for today is:

_____
_____
_____
_____
_____

NIGHT TIME RELAX AND RELEASE SESSION

How was your day? **Rate your day**

Amazing	Great	Good	OK	Bad	Terrible	It Sucked

I am grateful for, glad about, appreciative of, looking forward to:

1. _____

2. _____

3. _____

Reflection:

What did today teach you?

_____
_____
_____

What are you releasing from today?

_____
_____
_____

_____ I see you & I hear you.
Your Name

Take 3 deep long breaths in the nose & out of the mouth.

Center yourself in this thought/knowing that
"Everything is always working out for me."

Finish this sentence:

_____ I am so proud of you. Today you...
Your Name

_____
_____

Happy _____ *Today is My Day!*
(day of the week)

┌─ *Today I feel:* ─┐   ┌─ *Today I want to feel:* ─┐

I am grateful for, excited about, appreciative of, looking forward to:

1. _____
2. _____
3. _____

Morning Mantra:

Today is my day. I am in abundance. I have everything I need inside of me to Make Amazing Shit Happen. Everything is always working out for me. I am whole and complete. I look forward to GOD moving the universe on my behalf. I said it is so and so it is.

I will take the actions below in order to reach my desired feeling for today. I will practice in my good and better serving feeling as often as I need to or desire to today. I am committed to reaching and maintaining my desired feeling today.

1. _____
2. _____
3. _____

My intention for today is:

_____
_____
_____
_____

How was your day? **Rate your day**

| Amazing | Great | Good | OK | Bad | Terrible | It Sucked |

I am grateful for, glad about, appreciative of, looking forward to:

1. _____

2. _____

3. _____

Reflection:

What did today teach you?

_____
_____
_____

What are you releasing from today?

_____
_____
_____

_____ I see you & I hear you.
Your Name

Take 3 deep long breaths in the nose & out of the mouth.

Center yourself in this thought/knowing that
"Everything is always working out for me."

Finish this sentence:

_____ I am so proud of you. Today you...
Your Name

_____
_____

MORNING MINDSET SESSION

Happy _____ Today is My Day!
(day of the week)

┌─ Today I feel: ─┐ ┌─ Today I want to feel: ─┐

I am grateful for, excited about, appreciative of, looking forward to:

1. _____

2. _____

3. _____

Morning Mantra:

Today is my day. I am in abundance. I have everything I need inside of me to Make Amazing Shit Happen. Everything is always working out for me. I am whole and complete. I look forward to GOD moving the universe on my behalf. I said it is so and so it is.

I will take the actions below in order to reach my desired feeling for today. I will practice in my good and better serving feeling as often as I need to or desire to today. I am committed to reaching and maintaining my desired feeling today.

1. _____

2. _____

3. _____

My intention for today is:

_____
_____
_____
_____

NIGHT TIME RELAX AND RELEASE SESSION

How was your day? **Rate your day**

Amazing	Great	Good	OK	Bad	Terrible	It Sucked

I am grateful for, glad about, appreciative of, looking forward to:

1. _____

2. _____

3. _____

Reflection:

What did today teach you?

_____

_____

_____

What are you releasing from today?

_____

_____

_____

_____ I see you & I hear you.
Your Name

Take 3 deep long breaths in the nose & out of the mouth.

Center yourself in this thought/knowing that
"Everything is always working out for me."

Finish this sentence:

_____ I am so proud of you. Today you…
Your Name

_____

_____

Happy _____
(day of the week)

Today is My Day!

┌─── *Today I feel:* ───┐   ┌─── *Today I want to feel:* ───┐
│   │   │   │
│   │   │   │
│   │   │   │
│   │   │   │
└──────────────────────┘   └───────────────────────────────┘

I am grateful for, excited about, appreciative of, looking forward to:

1. _____

2. _____

3. _____

Morning Mantra:

Today is my day. I am in abundance. I have everything I need inside of me to Make Amazing Shit Happen. Everything is always working out for me. I am whole and complete. I look forward to GOD moving the universe on my behalf. I said it is so and so it is.

I will take the actions below in order to reach my desired feeling for today. I will practice in my good and better serving feeling as often as I need to or desire to today. I am committed to reaching and maintaining my desired feeling today.

1. _____

2. _____

3. _____

My intention for today is:

_____
_____
_____
_____

How was your day? Rate your day

:)	:|	:)	:)	:(	:(	><
Amazing	Great	Good	OK	Bad	Terrible	It Sucked

I am grateful for, glad about, appreciative of, looking forward to:

1. _____

2. _____

3. _____

Reflection:

What did today teach you?

_____
_____
_____

What are you releasing from today?

_____
_____
_____

_____ I see you & I hear you.
Your Name

Take 3 deep long breaths in the nose & out of the mouth.

Center yourself in this thought/knowing that
"Everything is always working out for me."

Finish this sentence:

_____ I am so proud of you. Today you...
Your Name

_____
_____

Happy _____ *Today is My Day!*
(day of the week)

Today I feel:

Today I want to feel:

I am grateful for, excited about, appreciative of, looking forward to:

1. _____
2. _____
3. _____

Morning Mantra:

Today is my day. I am in abundance. I have everything I need inside of me to Make Amazing Shit Happen. Everything is always working out for me. I am whole and complete. I look forward to GOD moving the universe on my behalf. I said it is so and so it is.

I will take the actions below in order to reach my desired feeling for today. I will practice in my good and better serving feeling as often as I need to or desire to today. I am committed to reaching and maintaining my desired feeling today.

1. _____
2. _____
3. _____

My intention for today is:

_____
_____
_____
_____

NIGHT TIME RELAX AND RELEASE SESSION

How was your day? **Rate your day**

😀   😐   🙂   🙂   🙁   😧   😣

Amazing   Great   Good   OK   Bad   Terrible   It Sucked

I am grateful for, glad about, appreciative of, looking forward to:

1. _____

2. _____

3. _____

Reflection:

What did today teach you?

_____
_____
_____

What are you releasing from today?

_____
_____
_____

_____ I see you & I hear you.
Your Name

Take 3 deep long breaths in the nose & out of the mouth.

Center yourself in this thought/knowing that
"Everything is always working out for me."

Finish this sentence:

_____ I am so proud of you. Today you...
Your Name

_____
_____

Happy _____ **(day of the week)** *Today is My Day!*

┌─── *Today I feel:* ───┐ ┌─── *Today I want to feel:* ───┐
│   │ │   │
│   │ │   │
│   │ │   │
└───────────────────────┘ └────────────────────────────────┘

I am grateful for, excited about, appreciative of, looking forward to:

1. _____

2. _____

3. _____

Morning Mantra:

Today is my day. I am in abundance. I have everything I need inside of me to Make Amazing Shit Happen. Everything is always working out for me. I am whole and complete. I look forward to GOD moving the universe on my behalf. I said it is so and so it is.

I will take the actions below in order to reach my desired feeling for today. I will practice in my good and better serving feeling as often as I need to or desire to today. I am committed to reaching and maintaining my desired feeling today.

1. _____

2. _____

3. _____

My intention for today is:

_____
_____
_____
_____

How was your day? Rate your day

:-D Amazing :-| Great :-) Good :-) OK :-(Bad :-(Terrible >-< It Sucked

I am grateful for, glad about, appreciative of, looking forward to:

1. _____

2. _____

3. _____

Reflection:

What did today teach you?

_____

_____

_____

What are you releasing from today?

_____

_____

_____

_____ I see you & I hear you.
Your Name

Take 3 deep long breaths in the nose & out of the mouth.

Center yourself in this thought/knowing that
"Everything is always working out for me."

Finish this sentence:

_____ I am so proud of you. Today you...
Your Name

_____

_____

Happy _____ Today is My Day!
(day of the week)

Today I feel:

Today I want to feel:

I am grateful for, excited about, appreciative of, looking forward to:

1. _____

2. _____

3. _____

Morning Mantra:

Today is my day. I am in abundance. I have everything I need inside of me to Make Amazing Shit Happen. Everything is always working out for me. I am whole and complete. I look forward to GOD moving the universe on my behalf. I said it is so and so it is.

I will take the actions below in order to reach my desired feeling for today. I will practice in my good and better serving feeling as often as I need to or desire to today. I am committed to reaching and maintaining my desired feeling today.

1. _____

2. _____

3. _____

My intention for today is:

_____
_____
_____
_____

NIGHT TIME RELAX AND RELEASE SESSION

How was your day? **Rate your day**

| Amazing | Great | Good | OK | Bad | Terrible | It Sucked |

I am grateful for, glad about, appreciative of, looking forward to:

1. _____
2. _____
3. _____

Reflection:

What did today teach you?

_____
_____
_____

What are you releasing from today?

_____
_____
_____

_____ I see you & I hear you.
Your Name

Take 3 deep long breaths in the nose & out of the mouth.

Center yourself in this thought/knowing that
"Everything is always working out for me."

Finish this sentence:

_____ I am so proud of you. Today you...
Your Name

_____
_____

Happy _____ *Today is My Day!*
(day of the week)

┌─── *Today I feel:* ───┐ ┌─── *Today I want to feel:* ───┐
│   │ │   │
│   │ │   │
│   │ │   │
│   │ │   │
└──────────────────────┘ └───────────────────────────────┘

I am grateful for, excited about, appreciative of, looking forward to:

1. _____

2. _____

3. _____

Morning Mantra:

Today is my day. I am in abundance. I have everything I need inside of me to Make Amazing Shit Happen. Everything is always working out for me. I am whole and complete. I look forward to GOD moving the universe on my behalf. I said it is so and so it is.

I will take the actions below in order to reach my desired feeling for today. I will practice in my good and better serving feeling as often as I need to or desire to today. I am committed to reaching and maintaining my desired feeling today.

1. _____

2. _____

3. _____

My intention for today is:

_____
_____
_____
_____

How was your day? **Rate your day**

Amazing	Great	Good	OK	Bad	Terrible	It Sucked

I am grateful for, glad about, appreciative of, looking forward to:

1. _____

2. _____

3. _____

Reflection:

What did today teach you?

_____

_____

_____

What are you releasing from today?

_____

_____

_____

_____

_____ I see you & I hear you.
Your Name

Take 3 deep long breaths in the nose & out of the mouth.

Center yourself in this thought/knowing that
"Everything is always working out for me."

Finish this sentence:

_____ I am so proud of you. Today you...
Your Name

_____

_____

MORNING MINDSET SESSION

Happy _____   *Today is My Day!*
                (day of the week)

┌─ *Today I feel:* ─┐   ┌─ *Today I want to feel:* ─┐
│   │   │   │
│   │   │   │
│   │   │   │
│   │   │   │
└───────────────────┘   └───────────────────────────┘

I am grateful for, excited about, appreciative of, looking forward to:

1. _____

2. _____

3. _____

Morning Mantra:

Today is my day. I am in abundance. I have everything I need inside of me to Make Amazing Shit Happen. Everything is always working out for me. I am whole and complete. I look forward to GOD moving the universe on my behalf. I said it is so and so it is.

I will take the actions below in order to reach my desired feeling for today. I will practice in my good and better serving feeling as often as I need to or desire to today. I am committed to reaching and maintaining my desired feeling today.

1. _____

2. _____

3. _____

My intention for today is:

_____
_____
_____
_____

NIGHT TIME RELAX AND RELEASE SESSION

How was your day? **Rate your day**

| Amazing | Great | Good | OK | Bad | Terrible | It Sucked |

I am grateful for, glad about, appreciative of, looking forward to:

1. _____

2. _____

3. _____

Reflection:

What did today teach you?

_____

_____

_____

What are you releasing from today?

_____

_____

_____

_____

_____ I see you & I hear you.
Your Name

Take 3 deep long breaths in the nose & out of the mouth.

Center yourself in this thought/knowing that
"Everything is always working out for me."

Finish this sentence:

_____ I am so proud of you. Today you...
Your Name

_____

_____

Happy _____
(day of the week)

Today is My Day!

┌─ Today I feel: ─┐   ┌─ Today I want to feel: ─┐
│   │   │   │
│   │   │   │
│   │   │   │
│   │   │   │
└─────────────────┘   └──────────────────────────┘

I am grateful for, excited about, appreciative of, looking forward to:

1. _____

2. _____

3. _____

Morning Mantra:

Today is my day. I am in abundance. I have everything I need inside of me to Make Amazing Shit Happen. Everything is always working out for me. I am whole and complete. I look forward to GOD moving the universe on my behalf. I said it is so and so it is.

I will take the actions below in order to reach my desired feeling for today. I will practice in my good and better serving feeling as often as I need to or desire to today. I am committed to reaching and maintaining my desired feeling today.

1. _____

2. _____

3. _____

My intention for today is:

_____
_____
_____
_____

How was your day? **Rate your day**

Amazing	Great	Good	OK	Bad	Terrible	It Sucked

I am grateful for, glad about, appreciative of, looking forward to:

1. _____

2. _____

3. _____

Reflection:

What did today teach you?

_____
_____
_____

What are you releasing from today?

_____
_____
_____

_____ I see you & I hear you.
Your Name

Take 3 deep long breaths in the nose & out of the mouth.

Center yourself in this thought/knowing that
"Everything is always working out for me."

Finish this sentence:

_____ I am so proud of you. Today you...
Your Name

_____
_____

MORNING MINDSET SESSION

Happy _____   Today is My Day!
(day of the week)

┌─ Today I feel: ─┐   ┌─ Today I want to feel: ─┐

I am grateful for, excited about, appreciative of, looking forward to:

1. _____

2. _____

3. _____

Morning Mantra:

Today is my day. I am in abundance. I have everything I need inside of me to Make Amazing Shit Happen. Everything is always working out for me. I am whole and complete. I look forward to GOD moving the universe on my behalf. I said it is so and so it is.

I will take the actions below in order to reach my desired feeling for today. I will practice in my good and better serving feeling as often as I need to or desire to today. I am committed to reaching and maintaining my desired feeling today.

1. _____

2. _____

3. _____

My intention for today is:

_____

_____

_____

_____

NIGHT TIME RELAX AND RELEASE SESSION

How was your day? **Rate your day**

:-)	:-|	^_^	:)	:-(	:-(	>_<
Amazing	Great	Good	OK	Bad	Terrible	It Sucked

I am grateful for, glad about, appreciative of, looking forward to:

1. _____

2. _____

3. _____

Reflection:

What did today teach you?

_____
_____
_____

What are you releasing from today?

_____
_____
_____

_____ I see you & I hear you.
Your Name

Take 3 deep long breaths in the nose & out of the mouth.

Center yourself in this thought/knowing that
"Everything is always working out for me."

Finish this sentence:

_____ I am so proud of you. Today you...
Your Name

_____
_____

Happy _____ Today is My Day!
(day of the week)

┌─ Today I feel: ─┐ ┌─ Today I want to feel: ─┐

I am grateful for, excited about, appreciative of, looking forward to:

1. _____

2. _____

3. _____

Morning Mantra:

Today is my day. I am in abundance. I have everything I need inside of me to Make Amazing Shit Happen. Everything is always working out for me. I am whole and complete. I look forward to GOD moving the universe on my behalf. I said it is so and so it is.

I will take the actions below in order to reach my desired feeling for today. I will practice in my good and better serving feeling as often as I need to or desire to to-day. I am committed to reaching and maintaining my desired feeling today.

1. _____

2. _____

3. _____

My intention for today is:

_____
_____
_____
_____

How was your day? **Rate your day**

Amazing	Great	Good	OK	Bad	Terrible	It Sucked

I am grateful for, glad about, appreciative of, looking forward to:

1. _____

2. _____

3. _____

Reflection:

What did today teach you?

_____
_____
_____

What are you releasing from today?

_____
_____
_____

_____ I see you & I hear you.
Your Name

Take 3 deep long breaths in the nose & out of the mouth.

Center yourself in this thought/knowing that
"Everything is always working out for me."

Finish this sentence:

_____ I am so proud of you. Today you...
Your Name

_____
_____

Happy _____ *Today is My Day!*
(day of the week)

┌─── *Today I feel:* ───┐ ┌─── *Today I want to feel:* ───┐
│   │ │   │
│   │ │   │
│   │ │   │
│   │ │   │
└──────────────────────┘ └───────────────────────────────┘

I am grateful for, excited about, appreciative of, looking forward to:

1. _____

2. _____

3. _____

Morning Mantra:

Today is my day. I am in abundance. I have everything I need inside of me to Make Amazing Shit Happen. Everything is always working out for me. I am whole and complete. I look forward to GOD moving the universe on my behalf. I said it is so and so it is.

I will take the actions below in order to reach my desired feeling for today. I will practice in my good and better serving feeling as often as I need to or desire to today. I am committed to reaching and maintaining my desired feeling today.

1. _____

2. _____

3. _____

My intention for today is:

_____
_____
_____
_____

NIGHT TIME RELAX AND RELEASE SESSION

How was your day? **Rate your day**

Amazing	Great	Good	OK	Bad	Terrible	It Sucked

I am grateful for, glad about, appreciative of, looking forward to:

1. _____

2. _____

3. _____

Reflection:

What did today teach you?

_____
_____
_____

What are you releasing from today?

_____
_____
_____

_____ I see you & I hear you.
Your Name

Take 3 deep long breaths in the nose & out of the mouth.

Center yourself in this thought/knowing that
"Everything is always working out for me."

Finish this sentence:

_____ I am so proud of you. Today you...
Your Name

_____
_____

Happy _____ Today is My Day!
(day of the week)

┌─── Today I feel: ───┐   ┌─── Today I want to feel: ───┐
│   │   │   │
│   │   │   │
│   │   │   │
│   │   │   │
└─────────────────────┘   └─────────────────────────────┘

I am grateful for, excited about, appreciative of, looking forward to:

1. _____

2. _____

3. _____

Morning Mantra:

Today is my day. I am in abundance. I have everything I need inside of me to Make Amazing Shit Happen. Everything is always working out for me. I am whole and complete. I look forward to GOD moving the universe on my behalf. I said it is so and so it is.

I will take the actions below in order to reach my desired feeling for today. I will practice in my good and better serving feeling as often as I need to or desire to today. I am committed to reaching and maintaining my desired feeling today.

1. _____

2. _____

3. _____

My intention for today is:

_____
_____
_____
_____

How was your day? Rate your day

| Amazing | Great | Good | OK | Bad | Terrible | It Sucked |

I am grateful for, glad about, appreciative of, looking forward to:

1. _____

2. _____

3. _____

Reflection:

What did today teach you?

_____
_____
_____

What are you releasing from today?

_____
_____
_____
_____

_____ I see you & I hear you.
Your Name

Take 3 deep long breaths in the nose & out of the mouth.

Center yourself in this thought/knowing that
"Everything is always working out for me."

Finish this sentence:

_____ I am so proud of you. Today you...
Your Name

_____
_____

MORNING MINDSET SESSION

Happy _____ *Today is My Day!*
(day of the week)

Today I feel:

Today I want to feel:

I am grateful for, excited about, appreciative of, looking forward to:

1. _____
2. _____
3. _____

Morning Mantra:

Today is my day. I am in abundance. I have everything I need inside of me to Make Amazing Shit Happen. Everything is always working out for me. I am whole and complete. I look forward to GOD moving the universe on my behalf. I said it is so and so it is.

I will take the actions below in order to reach my desired feeling for today. I will practice in my good and better serving feeling as often as I need to or desire to today. I am committed to reaching and maintaining my desired feeling today.

1. _____
2. _____
3. _____

My intention for today is:

_____
_____
_____
_____

NIGHT TIME RELAX AND RELEASE SESSION

How was your day? **Rate your day**

Amazing	Great	Good	OK	Bad	Terrible	It Sucked

I am grateful for, glad about, appreciative of, looking forward to:

1. _____

2. _____

3. _____

Reflection:

What did today teach you?

_____
_____
_____

What are you releasing from today?

_____
_____
_____

_____ I see you & I hear you.
Your Name

Take 3 deep long breaths in the nose & out of the mouth.

Center yourself in this thought/knowing that
"Everything is always working out for me."

Finish this sentence:

_____ I am so proud of you. Today you...
Your Name

_____
_____

Happy _____ *Today is My Day!*
(day of the week)

┌─ *Today I feel:* ─┐   ┌─ *Today I want to feel:* ─┐

I am grateful for, excited about, appreciative of, looking forward to:

1. _____

2. _____

3. _____

Morning Mantra:

Today is my day. I am in abundance. I have everything I need inside of me to Make Amazing Shit Happen. Everything is always working out for me. I am whole and complete. I look forward to GOD moving the universe on my behalf. I said it is so and so it is.

I will take the actions below in order to reach my desired feeling for today. I will practice in my good and better serving feeling as often as I need to or desire to today. I am committed to reaching and maintaining my desired feeling today.

1. _____

2. _____

3. _____

My intention for today is:

_____
_____
_____
_____

How was your day? **Rate your day**

Amazing	Great	Good	OK	Bad	Terrible	It Sucked

I am grateful for, glad about, appreciative of, looking forward to:

1. _____

2. _____

3. _____

Reflection:

What did today teach you?

_____

_____

_____

What are you releasing from today?

_____

_____

_____

_____

_____ I see you & I hear you.
Your Name

Take 3 deep long breaths in the nose & out of the mouth.

Center yourself in this thought/knowing that
"Everything is always working out for me."

Finish this sentence:

_____ I am so proud of you. Today you...
Your Name

_____

_____

MORNING MINDSET SESSION

Happy _____   *Today is My Day!*
(day of the week)

┌─── *Today I feel:* ───┐   ┌─── *Today I want to feel:* ───┐
│   │   │   │
│   │   │   │
│   │   │   │
│   │   │   │
└───────────────────────┘   └───────────────────────────────┘

I am grateful for, excited about, appreciative of, looking forward to:

1. _____

2. _____

3. _____

Morning Mantra:

Today is my day. I am in abundance. I have everything I need inside of me to Make Amazing Shit Happen. Everything is always working out for me. I am whole and complete. I look forward to GOD moving the universe on my behalf. I said it is so and so it is.

I will take the actions below in order to reach my desired feeling for today. I will practice in my good and better serving feeling as often as I need to or desire to today. I am committed to reaching and maintaining my desired feeling today.

1. _____

2. _____

3. _____

My intention for today is:

_____

_____

_____

_____

NIGHT TIME RELAX AND RELEASE SESSION

How was your day? Rate your day

Amazing	Great	Good	OK	Bad	Terrible	It Sucked

I am grateful for, glad about, appreciative of, looking forward to:

1. _____

2. _____

3. _____

Reflection:

What did today teach you?

_____

_____

_____

What are you releasing from today?

_____

_____

_____

_____

_____ I see you & I hear you.

Your Name

Take 3 deep long breaths in the nose & out of the mouth.

Center yourself in this thought/knowing that
"Everything is always working out for me."

Finish this sentence:

_____ I am so proud of you. Today you...

Your Name

_____

_____

Happy _____ *Today is My Day!*
(day of the week)

┌─ *Today I feel:* ─┐ ┌─ *Today I want to feel:* ─┐

I am grateful for, excited about, appreciative of, looking forward to:

1. _____

2. _____

3. _____

Morning Mantra:

Today is my day. I am in abundance. I have everything I need inside of me to Make Amazing Shit Happen. Everything is always working out for me. I am whole and complete. I look forward to GOD moving the universe on my behalf. I said it is so and so it is.

I will take the actions below in order to reach my desired feeling for today. I will practice in my good and better serving feeling as often as I need to or desire to today. I am committed to reaching and maintaining my desired feeling today.

1. _____

2. _____

3. _____

My intention for today is:

_____
_____
_____
_____

NIGHT TIME RELAX AND RELEASE SESSION

How was your day? **Rate your day**

Amazing	Great	Good	OK	Bad	Terrible	It Sucked

I am grateful for, glad about, appreciative of, looking forward to:

1. _____

2. _____

3. _____

Reflection:

What did today teach you?

_____
_____
_____

What are you releasing from today?

_____
_____
_____
_____

_____ I see you & I hear you.
Your Name

Take 3 deep long breaths in the nose & out of the mouth.

Center yourself in this thought/knowing that
"Everything is always working out for me."

Finish this sentence:

_____ I am so proud of you. Today you...
Your Name

_____
_____

Happy _____
(day of the week)

Today is My Day!

┌─ Today I feel: ─┐   ┌─ Today I want to feel: ─┐

I am grateful for, excited about, appreciative of, looking forward to:

1. _____

2. _____

3. _____

Morning Mantra:

Today is my day. I am in abundance. I have everything I need inside of me to Make Amazing Shit Happen. Everything is always working out for me. I am whole and complete. I look forward to GOD moving the universe on my behalf. I said it is so and so it is.

I will take the actions below in order to reach my desired feeling for today. I will practice in my good and better serving feeling as often as I need to or desire to today. I am committed to reaching and maintaining my desired feeling today.

1. _____

2. _____

3. _____

My intention for today is:

_____
_____
_____
_____

NIGHT TIME RELAX AND RELEASE SESSION

How was your day? **Rate your day**

Amazing	Great	Good	OK	Bad	Terrible	It Sucked

I am grateful for, glad about, appreciative of, looking forward to:

1. _____

2. _____

3. _____

Reflection:

What did today teach you?

_____

_____

_____

What are you releasing from today?

_____

_____

_____

_____ I see you & I hear you.
Your Name

Take 3 deep long breaths in the nose & out of the mouth.

Center yourself in this thought/knowing that
"Everything is always working out for me."

Finish this sentence:

_____ I am so proud of you. Today you...
Your Name

_____

_____

Happy _____ *Today is My Day!*
(day of the week)

⎡ *Today I feel:* ⎤   ⎡ *Today I want to feel:* ⎤

I am grateful for, excited about, appreciative of, looking forward to:

1. _____

2. _____

3. _____

Morning Mantra:

Today is my day. I am in abundance. I have everything I need inside of me to Make Amazing Shit Happen. Everything is always working out for me. I am whole and complete. I look forward to GOD moving the universe on my behalf. I said it is so and so it is.

I will take the actions below in order to reach my desired feeling for today. I will practice in my good and better serving feeling as often as I need to or desire to today. I am committed to reaching and maintaining my desired feeling today.

1. _____

2. _____

3. _____

My intention for today is:

_____
_____
_____
_____

How was your day? **Rate your day**

| Amazing | Great | Good | OK | Bad | Terrible | It Sucked |

I am grateful for, glad about, appreciative of, looking forward to:

1. _____

2. _____

3. _____

Reflection:

What did today teach you?

_____
_____
_____

What are you releasing from today?

_____
_____
_____
_____

_____ I see you & I hear you.
Your Name

Take 3 deep long breaths in the nose & out of the mouth.

Center yourself in this thought/knowing that
"Everything is always working out for me."

Finish this sentence:

_____ I am so proud of you. Today you...
Your Name

_____
_____

Happy _____
(day of the week)

Today is My Day!

┌─── *Today I feel:* ───┐   ┌─── *Today I want to feel:* ───┐
│   │   │   │
│   │   │   │
│   │   │   │
└───────────────────────┘   └────────────────────────────────┘

I am grateful for, excited about, appreciative of, looking forward to:

1. _____

2. _____

3. _____

Morning Mantra:

Today is my day. I am in abundance. I have everything I need inside of me to Make Amazing Shit Happen. Everything is always working out for me. I am whole and complete. I look forward to GOD moving the universe on my behalf. I said it is so and so it is.

I will take the actions below in order to reach my desired feeling for today. I will practice in my good and better serving feeling as often as I need to or desire to today. I am committed to reaching and maintaining my desired feeling today.

1. _____

2. _____

3. _____

My intention for today is:

_____

_____

_____

_____

NIGHT TIME RELAX AND RELEASE SESSION

How was your day? **Rate your day**

😃　　😀　　🙂　　🙂　　🙁　　☹️　　😣
Amazing　　Great　　Good　　OK　　Bad　　Terrible　　It Sucked

I am grateful for, glad about, appreciative of, looking forward to:

1. _____

2. _____

3. _____

Reflection:

What did today teach you?

_____
_____
_____

What are you releasing from today?

_____
_____
_____

_____ I see you & I hear you.
　　　　Your Name

Take 3 deep long breaths in the nose & out of the mouth.

Center yourself in this thought/knowing that
"Everything is always working out for me."

Finish this sentence:

_____ I am so proud of you. Today you...
　　Your Name

_____
_____

Happy _____   *Today is My Day!*
(day of the week)

┌─────────────┐   ┌─────────────┐
Today I feel: *Today I want to feel:*

└─────────────┘   └─────────────┘

I am grateful for, excited about, appreciative of, looking forward to:

1. _____

2. _____

3. _____

Morning Mantra:

Today is my day. I am in abundance. I have everything I need inside of me to Make Amazing Shit Happen. Everything is always working out for me. I am whole and complete. I look forward to GOD moving the universe on my behalf. I said it is so and so it is.

I will take the actions below in order to reach my desired feeling for today. I will practice in my good and better serving feeling as often as I need to or desire to today. I am committed to reaching and maintaining my desired feeling today.

1. _____

2. _____

3. _____

My intention for today is:

_____

_____

_____

_____

How was your day? **Rate your day**

Amazing	Great	Good	OK	Bad	Terrible	It Sucked

I am grateful for, glad about, appreciative of, looking forward to:

1. _____

2. _____

3. _____

Reflection:

What did today teach you?

_____
_____
_____

What are you releasing from today?

_____
_____
_____

_____ I see you & I hear you.
Your Name

Take 3 deep long breaths in the nose & out of the mouth.

Center yourself in this thought/knowing that
"Everything is always working out for me."

Finish this sentence:

_____ I am so proud of you. Today you...
Your Name

_____
_____

Made in the USA
Columbia, SC
16 September 2020